Russ Shipton's

KEYBOARD & PIANO
Course
Book two

For Tracey, an inspiration...
"Uni-keyboard" notation by Russ Shipton
The special form of notation used in this book was devised by Russ Shipton.
It is copyright and can be used by permission only.

First Published 1992
© International Music Publications

International Music Publications, Southend Road, Woodford Green, Essex IG8 8HN, England

215-2-727

BOOK 2

The second book of "Russ Shipton's Keyboard & Piano Course" will take you a stage further along the road to becoming a versatile and competent player. The patterns and styles looked at in Book 1 are developed, using the same simplified notation and more popular songs for illustration and practice.

Swing Style

Another important category of playing is introduced in Book 2 - the swing style. Many songs are performed with a swing in the rhythm, and can be found in different areas of music, including jazz, blues, folk, rock and pop.

More Keys & Chords

Two more major keys are introduced in this book: **F** major, together with its relative key of **D** minor, and **D** major; and your chord repertoire will increase by learning many dominant, minor and major 7th chords. You'll also get your first taste of syncopation (off-beat stress), and bass runs are used to spice up the accompaniments.

Layout

As in Book 1, the techniques and patterns given in Book 2 are analysed thoroughly before each featured song. The analysis and song are always presented on facing pages, so no turning over is necessary and practising is easier. Titles of additional practice songs are listed after each featured song, with the chord sequences for some of them given at the back of the book.

MATCHING CASSETTE

An accompanying cassette is available for use with Book 2. It is produced and presented by Russ Shipton, with all the chords, runs, rhythm patterns and songs recorded note-for-note. To make learning easier, the rhythm patterns and song accompaniments are demonstrated at two speeds: slowly, then up-to-tempo. You can check your understanding of the music and your standard of playing.

One track of the stereo recording contains *only* the keyboard part, while the second track contains the other band instruments. First you can hear and play along with the keyboard track, and then when you're ready you can enjoy playing along with the band!

The material in the course is gently graded, so if you practise a little each day you'll be able to progress quickly.

Enjoy your playing,

Russ Shipton

Contents

SONGS FEATURED IN THIS BOOK

Abilene	Momma Don't Allow
By The Time I Get To Phoenix	Moon River
Carrickfergus	Mr. Bojangles
Congratulations	Sacrifice
Greensleeves	Scarborough Fair
Help Me Make It Through The Night	Stand By Me
Hi Ho Silver Lining	Sunrise, Sunset
In Dublin's Fair City	Three Times A Lady
King Of The Road	Will You Go, Lassie, Go?

MAJOR KEYS

In Book1 all the songs were written in a 'major' key. Most of the accompaniments that you played were in the key of **C** major - where the **c** note is the main or key note, and the **C** major chord is the most important chord. Our ears expect the melody to end on a **c** note, and the **C** major chord to end the accompaniment. The notes expected in *both* melody and accompanying chords are summarised by the **C** major scale:

*The **C** Major Scale:*

c   d   e   f   g   a   b   c

Expected Chords:

C   Dm   Em   F   G   Am

The chord 'built on' the seventh note of the major scale (**b** here) is a diminished chord - it's not shown because it's rarely used. We'll look at the diminished chord later in the course.

Playing The C Major Scale

Play the **C** major scale notes several times (with your right hand), and then go through the chords. Your ear will soon become accustomed to the note relationship or 'tonality' of a major key.

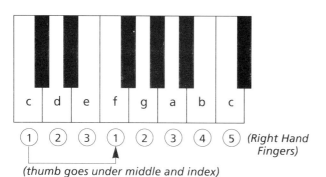

① ② ③ ① ② ③ ④ ⑤ *(Right Hand Fingers)*

(thumb goes under middle and index)

The right hand fingering given below the notes will help you to play the scale smoothly - pass your thumb ① under the index ② and middle ③ fingers for the **f** note. When playing the scale downwards in pitch from higher to lower **c**, pass your middle finger ③ *over* the thumb ①.

The Key Of G Major

In this key, the **g** note is the main or key note (also referred to sometimes as the 'tonic' note), and the **G** major chord is the most important chord. Our ears will expect the melody to end on a **g** note and the accompaniment to end on a **G** chord.

*The **G** Major Scale:*

g   a   b   c   d   e   f#   g

Expected Chords:

G   Am   Bm   C   D   Em

The last two song accompaniments of Book 1 were in the key of **G** major. The expected notes and chords in this key (and all other major keys) have exactly the same relationship and therefore 'feel' as those shown for **C** major.

Play through the **G** major scale notes and then chords - you'll notice the strong similarity to the **C** major scale notes and chords.

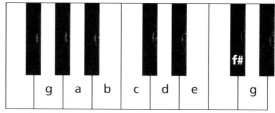

(Use the same fingering as for the C scale)

Sharps & Flats

Only the **C** major scale consists of just white key notes. The notes of the **C** major scale and the chords made up from them involve no sharp (#) or flat (♭) notes i.e. no black keys on the keyboard. The other major keys involve one or more black key notes. The key of **G** major involves the **f#** note, as you can see above.

Note Intervals Of The Major Scale

Every major scale involves the same intervals between notes. These are shown with the general major scale that we learn when young:

The General Major Scale:

Doh	Ray	Me	Fah	Soh	Lah	Te	Doh
tone	tone	semi-tone	tone	tone	tone	semi-tone	

The C Major Scale:

c	d	e	f	g	a	b	c
		semi-tone				semi-tone	

The G Major Scale:

g	a	b	c	d	e	f#	g
		semi-tone				semi-tone	

Tones & Semitones

In music, the smallest interval of pitch is a semitone. On the keyboard, moving an interval of a semitone means going from one key to the next one along, whether black or white:

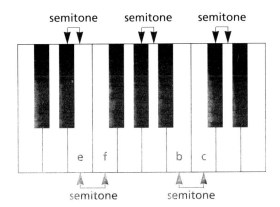

The C major scale involves no sharp or flat notes because there is no note between e & f and between b & c i.e. these notes are a semitone apart, and they happen to fall at the semitone positions of the C major scale.

MINOR KEYS

In Book 1 none of the songs was written in a 'minor' key. Though the majority of music today is written in a major key, you'll come across many songs written in a minor key - like the first song in the book, "Greensleeves".

The difference between music written in a minor rather than major key is created by the different intervals between the scale notes. Here is the **A** minor scale, for example:

The A Minor Scale:

a	b	c	d	e	f	g	a
tone	semi-tone	tone	tone	semi-tone	tone	tone	

Expected Chords:

Am		C	Dm	Em	F	G

In the key of **A** minor, our ears expect the melody to end on an **a** note and the accompaniment to end on an **Am** chord.

Play through the notes of the **A** minor scale to get the feel of the minor tonality. Go through the chords too. The **a** note is the key note, and it has a different interval relationship with the other notes than the key note of a major key.

Relative Major & Minor Keys

When you play the songs in this and the final two books of the course, you'll notice the similarity of notes and chords in certain major and minor keys. This is because they are 'relative' to each other. For example, the **C** major scale notes and the **A** minor scale notes - if you check above - are exactly the same. They are in a different order, which produces the changed sound or tonality.

Though the expected notes and chords in the keys of **C** major and **A** minor are the same, some variations to the notes and chords in minor keys are very common today, as will be demonstrated and explained.

A NEW 3-BEAT RHYTHM PATTERN

In Book 1 the simple chord style involved just a right hand chord on each beat of the bar. When playing on your own, one or more notes can also be played *between* beats to fill out the sound a bit.

right hand chords   left hand note

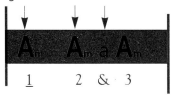

Am	Am	a	Am
1	2	&	3

7TH CHORDS

In Book 1 you learnt basic 3-note major and minor chords. In this book you'll be using some 7th chords, which involve another note. Try the **E** & **E7** chords:

The E(7) Chord

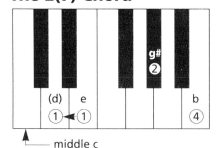

E = e g# b

E7= add d note

— middle c

In the accompaniment for "Greensleeves", you'll need to change from an **E** chord to **E7**: just move your thumb ① from the **e** note to the **d** note, as shown. Notice that in the key of **A** minor, **E** (or **E7**) is often used instead of the 'expected' **Em**.

Chord/Note Fingering

The **Am** in the verse should be fingered in the middle of the keyboard, using **middle c**. For the left hand notes, start by playing the low **a** note with your little finger ⑤, then the low **c** with your middle finger ③, **g** with the thumb ①, and so on, trying not to move more than necessary.

Greensleeves

When you can play the accompaniment smoothly, try humming or singing the melody:

Alas my love, you do me wrong, to cast me off discourteously
a c d e f e d b g a b c a ag#a b g# e

Though I have loved you for so long, delighting in   your company
  a c d   e f e d b g d   b c b a g#f# g# a a a

Greensleeves was all my joy, Greensleeves was my delight
  g   g f# e d b g a b   c a a g# a b g# e

Greensleeves was my heart of gold
  g   g f# e d b g a

Oh who but my sweet lady Greensleeves.
  b   c b a g# f#g# a   a

GREENSLEEVES

Traditional, arranged by Russ Shipton

Verse															
Am	Am	a	Am	C	C	c	C	G	G	g	G	Em	Em	e	Em
1	2	&	3	1	2	&	3	1	2	&	3	1	2	&	3
(A-) las,			my	love,			you	do			me	wrong			to

F	F	f	F	Dm	Dm	d	Dm	E	E	e	E	E7	E7	e	E7
1	2	&	3	1	2	&	3	1	2	&	3	1	2	&	3
cast			me	o - ff	dis		- court	-			eous	- ly,			though

Simple Chord Style

GREENSLEEVES
(Continued)

Am	Am a Am	C	C c C	G	G g G	Em	Em e Em
1	2 & 3	1	2 & 3	1	2 & 3	1	2 & 3
I	have	lov	- ed you	for	so	lo	- ng, de -

F	F f F	E	E e E	Am	Am a Am	Am	Am a Am
1	2 & 3	1	2 & 3	1	2 & 3	1	2 & 3
li	- ght - ing	i	- n your	comp	- an	- y.	

Chorus

C	C c C	C	C c C	G	G g G	G	G g G
1	2 & 3	1	2 & 3	1	2 & 3	1	2 & 3
Green	-	sle	- eves was	all	my	jo	- y,

Am	Am a Am	F	F f F	E	E e E	E_7	E_7 e E_7
1	2 & 3	1	2 & 3	1	2 & 3	1	2 & 3
Green	-	sle	- eves was	my	de	- light.	

C	C c C	C	C c C	G	G g G	G	G g G
1	2 & 3	1	2 & 3	1	2 & 3	1	2 & 3
Green	-	sleeves was	my	heart	of	go - ld,	oh

F	F f F	E	E e E_7	Am	Am a Am	Am	Am a Am
1	2 & 3	1	2 & 3	1	2 & 3	1	2 & 3
who	but my	sweet	la - dy	Green	-	sleeves.	

ADDITIONAL SONGS

Here are some songs that you can try after you've mastered "Greensleeves". They are all written in a minor key and can be played with the same 3-beat rhythm pattern. The chord sequences for most of these songs are given in the back of the book with the other verses of "Greensleeves".

MORNING HAS BROKEN (Cat Stevens)
THE FIRST NOEL (Traditional)
IN THE PINES (Leadbelly)
THE QUEEN OF HEARTS (Traditional)
NIGHTS IN WHITE SATIN (The Moody Blues)
THE HOUSE OF THE RISING SUN (Traditional).

ANOTHER 3-BEAT PATTERN

The main pattern for "Moon River" involves *two* left hand notes:

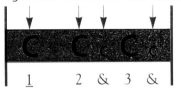

Watch out for the slight pattern variations, and also the chord changes within bars (bars 8, 14, 15 & 16).

More 7th Chords

As for the E7 chord, move your thumb ① across one key to the left for the B7, A7 & G7 chords:

The B(7) Chord

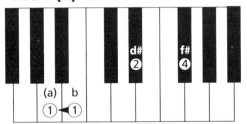

The A(7) Chord

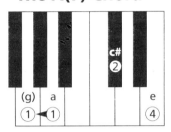

The G(7) Chord

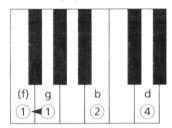

Chord/Note Fingering

Use root chord positions at first. The Am, B, B7 & C can be played using **middle c** or across it. Other chords can be played above **middle c**. Then try inversions to reduce right hand movement. For example, use the 1st inversion of **Am** in bar 2 (c e a), followed by the 2nd inversion of **F** in bar 3 (c f a). For the low left hand notes, start with your middle finger ③ for the **c** note, then little finger ⑤ for the **a** and thumb ① for **f**, and so on, keeping the left hand movement to a minimum.

Moon River

Moon river, wider than a mile, I'm crossing you in style some day
g d c b a g f g c b a g f g c d

Old dream-maker, you heartbreaker
e c g e d c g e

Wherever you're going, I'm going your way
d c e g c b a b a a

Two drifters off to see the world, there's such a lot of world to see
g d c b c g f g c b a g f g c d

We're after the same rainbow's end, waiting round the bend
e c e g c d c g b a g f g

My Huckleberry friend, moon river and me.
c b a g f g c f d e c

MOON RIVER

Words by Johnny Mercer, Music by Henry Mancini

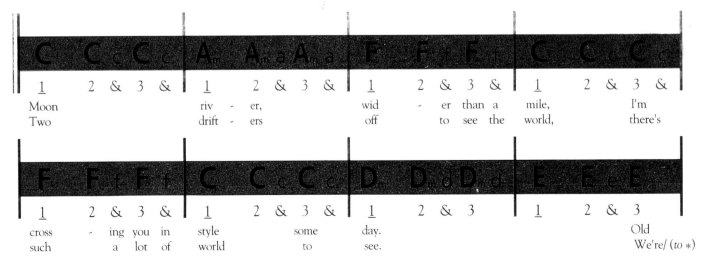

MOON RIVER
(Continued)

Am Am a Am a	C C c C c	F F f F f	Em Em e Em e
1 2 & 3 &	1 2 & 3 &	1 2 & 3 &	1 2 & 3 &
dream	mak - er, you	heart -	break - er, where -

(Repeat bars 1-8)

Am Am a Am a	B B b B7	Em A A7 a	Dm Dm d G
1 2 & 3 &	1 2 & 3	1 2 & 3	1 2 & 3
ev - er you're	going,	I'm go - ing your	way.

*

Am Am a Am a	C C c C c	Am Am a Am a	F F f F f
1 2 & 3 &	1 2 & 3 &	1 2 & 3 &	1 2 & 3 &
aft -	er the	same	rain - bow's

C C c C c	F F f F f	C C c C c	F F f F f
1 2 & 3 &	1 2 & 3 &	1 2 & 3 &	1 2 & 3 &
end,	waiting round the	bend,	my Huckleberry

C C c C c	Am Am a Am a	Dm Dm d Dm d	G G g G7
1 2 & 3 &	1 2 & 3 &	1 2 & 3 &	1 2 & 3
friend,	moon	riv - er	and

C C c C c	Dm Dm d Dm d	G G g G g	G7 G7 g G7
1 2 & 3 &	1 2 & 3 &	1 2 & 3 &	1 2 & 3
me.			

ADDITIONAL SONGS

Other well-known songs that can be played with similar chords and rhythm pattern are listed opposite. The chord sequences for some of them are given in the back of the book.

FLY ME TO THE MOON (Frank Sinatra)
AMAZING GRACE (Judy Collins)
SAY WONDERFUL THINGS (Ronnie Carroll)
TURN AROUND (Harry Belafonte)
DIANE (The Bachelors)
TEARS (Ken Dodd)
OLD SHEP (Elvis Presley)
YOU LIGHT UP MY LIFE (Debbie Boone).

A NEW 4-BEAT PATTERN

The 4-beat pattern at the start of Book 1 can be filled out with one or more left hand notes between the four chords played on the beats:

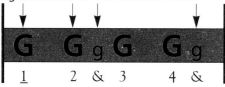

right hand chords   low left hand notes

G	G	g	G	G	g
1	2	&	3	4	&

This pattern is used throughout the accompaniment for "Help Me Make It Through The Night", apart from the opening bar of the verses - play the **D7** chord on the first beat of the bar and let it ring on till the next bar. Take the rhythm nice and steady, stressing the first beat of each bar slightly more than the others, but all the chords should be played evenly and deliberately.

Another 7th Chord Fingering

A new chord, **D7**, is used in the next accompaniment. This chord, like the **E7**, **B7**, **A7** & **G7** can be played with or without the root note. Here is the **D7** without the root:

The D7 Chord (no root)

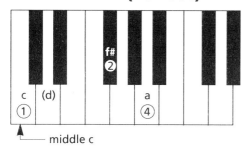

— middle c

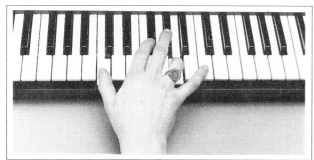

You can use your thumb ① to press down both **c** & **d** notes by turning it to the left a little, as shown in the photo. (If you prefer, use four fingers i.e. thumb ①, index ②, middle ③ and little finger ⑤.)

The D7 Chord (with root)

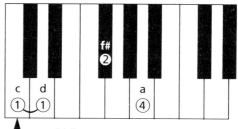

— middle c

KRIS KRISTOFFERSON

Help Me Make It Through The Night

Take the ribbon from your hair, shake it loose and let it fall
g b c b a b d b b c   b b a g

Laying soft upon my skin, like the shadows on the wall
a b c a a g f# a b c b a g b

(Melody for next 2 lines same as first 2)

Help me make it through the night
c   c   b   a   g   f# g

I don't care what's right or wrong, I don't try to understand
g g e   e   f#   g g g a g g e d

Let the devil take tomorrow, Lord, tonight I need a friend.
e f# g g g   g f# e   e   f# g g f# e   d

Simple Chord Style

HELP ME MAKE IT THROUGH THE NIGHT

Words and Music by Kris Kristofferson

(Hold)   Verse

| D₇ | G G g G G g | G G g G G g |

1   2 & 3   4 &

Verse 1. Take the ribbon from your hair,   shake it loose and let it
Verse 2. Come and lay down by my side,   till the early morning

| C C c C C c | Am Am a Am Am a | D D d D D d |

fall,   laying soft upon my skin,
light.   All I'm asking is your time,

(to Verse 2)   Middle Section

| D₇ D₇ d D₇ D₇ d | G G g G G g | G₇ G₇ g G₇ G₇ g |

like the shadows on the wall.
help me make it thru' the night.   /   I don't care what's right or

| C C c C C c | C C c C C c | G G g G G g |

wrong,   I don't try to un - der - stand.

| G G g G G g | A A a A A a | A₇ A₇ a A₇ A₇ a |

Let the devil take to - morrow,   Lord, to - night I need a

| D D d D D d |

friend.

ADDITIONAL SONGS

Here are more songs that can be played with the same rhythm pattern (and the chords you know).

MY WAY (Frank Sinatra)
GREEN GREEN GRASS OF HOME (Tom Jones)

THE WATER IS WIDE (Traditional)
OLD MAN RIVER (Traditional)
HEY JUDE (The Beatles)
IMAGINE (John Lennon)
IN THE AIR TONIGHT (Phil Collins).

11

THE KEY OF F MAJOR

Another popular key for keyboard players is the key of F major. Like the key of G major, this involves just one black key:

F Major Scale: f   g   a   b♭   c   d   e   f

Expected Chords: F   Gm   Am   B♭   C   Dm

To keep the correct major scale intervals between notes (i.e. tone tone semitone, tone tone tone semitone), the **b** note must be lowered a semitone to **b♭**. This is the same pitch as **a#**, and is the black key between the **a** and **b** white keys.

More Chords

You've already seen the **F, Am, C & Dm** chords in the keys of **C** and **G** major; here are the **Gm** and **B♭** chords in root position:

The Gm Chord

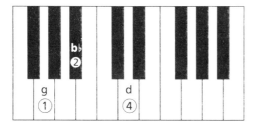

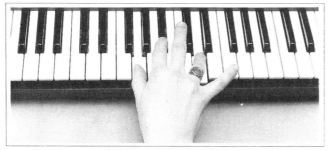

The middle chord note (the '3rd') creates a major or minor chord. To turn a root position major chord into a minor chord, just move your index finger ② one key to the left (whether black or white).

Move your hand across the keys a little for the B♭ :

The B♭ Chord

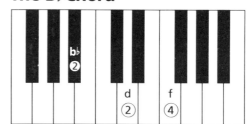

Pattern Variations

Slight pattern changes create more interest. The next accompaniment includes variations in the position and number of left hand notes. Count each bar carefully!

Chord/Note Fingering

Try root chord fingerings to begin with. The **C & B♭** chords can be played using **middle c** and across **middle c**, the others above **middle c**. Hold your left hand so the thumb ① takes the **f** note, the middle finger ③ the **c** note, the little finger ⑤ the **b♭** note, and so on. Experiment with inversions later - the 2nd inversion **F** (c f a) will cut down on your right hand movement, for example.

Will You Go, Lassie, Go?

Oh the summer time is coming, and the trees are sweetly blooming
f   g   a   a   g   f   d   f   a   c   d   d   d   c   a   c

And the wild mountain thyme, grows around the blooming heather
a   c   d   c   a   g   f   g   a   b♭   a   g   f   d   f

Will you go, lassie, go? *(Melody of chorus is like the verse)*
f   d   c   d   f   f

WILL YOU GO, LASSIE, GO?

Traditional, arranged by Russ Shipton

Simple Chord Style

WILL YOU GO, LASSIE, GO?
(Continued)

F		F	f	F	f	F		B♭		B♭	b♭	C		C	c	D♭	D♭	d	D♭	d	D♭
<u>1</u>		2	&	3	&	4		<u>1</u>		2	&	3		4	&	<u>1</u>		2	&	3	&	4

blooming,   and the   wild,   mount - ain   thyme   grows a -

| G♭ | | G♭ | g | G♭ | g | D♭ | | B♭ | | B♭ | b♭ | B♭ | b♭ | B♭ | | F | | F | f | B♭ | | B♭ | b♭ |

Chorus

| <u>1</u> | | 2 | & | 3 | & | 4 | | <u>1</u> | | 2 | & | 3 | & | 4 | | <u>1</u> | | 2 | & | 3 | | 4 | & |

round   the bloom - ing   heather.   Will you   go,   lassie,

| F | | F | f | F | f | F | | B♭ | | B♭ | b♭ | B♭ | b♭ | B♭ | | F | | F | f | F | f | F |
| <u>1</u> | | 2 | & | 3 | & | 4 | | <u>1</u> | | 2 | & | 3 | & | 4 | | <u>1</u> | | 2 | & | 3 | & | 4 |

go?   And we'll   all   go   to - gether,   to pluck

| B♭ | | B♭ | b♭ | C | | C | c | D♭ | D♭ | d | D♭ | d | D♭ | | G♭ | | G♭ | g | G♭ | g | D♭ |
| <u>1</u> | | 2 | & | 3 | | 4 | & | <u>1</u> | | 2 | & | 3 | & | 4 | | <u>1</u> | | 2 | & | 3 | & | 4 |

wild   mount - ain   thyme,   all a - round   the bloom - ing

| B♭ | | B♭ | b♭ | B♭ | b♭ | B♭ | | F | | F | f | B♭ | | B♭ | b♭ | F | | F | f | F | f | F |
| <u>1</u> | | 2 | & | 3 | & | 4 | | <u>1</u> | | 2 | & | 3 | | 4 | & | <u>1</u> | | 2 | & | 3 | | 4 | & |

heather.   Will you   go,   lassie,   go?

ADDITIONAL SONGS

Ballads you can play with the same kind of rhythm pattern are listed opposite. Try playing one or two in the key of **F**. The chord sequences for some of these songs are given at the back of the book, together with the other verses for "Will You Go, Lassie, Go?"

EVERYTHING I OWN (Bread)
KUM BY YAH (Traditional)
WHEN A CHILD IS BORN (Johnny Mathis)
THE LEAVING OF LIVERPOOL (Traditional)
ETERNAL FLAME (The Bangles)
LET IT BE (The Beatles).

Bass-Chord Style

ALTERNATING BASS PATTERN

In Book 1, alternating bass notes were used in a 4-beat bass-chord accompaniment, on the first and third beats of each bar. In a 3-beat rhythm, different bass notes can start alternate bars:

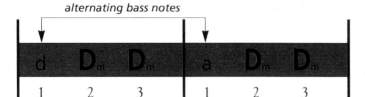

alternating bass notes

d	D$_m$	D$_m$	a	D$_m$	D$_m$
<u>1</u>	2	3	<u>1</u>	2	3

Try stopping the chords slightly to get a 'springy' effect.

THE KEY OF D MINOR

The relative key of **F** major is **D** minor. Thus the expected notes will be essentially the same:

D Minor Scale: d   e   f   g   a   b♭   c   d

Expected chords: Dm   F Gm Am B♭ C

The expected chords include **Am**. As you saw in the key of **A** minor, the chord built on the 5th scale note is often changed to major, so in the key of **D** minor, the **A** or **A7** chord may be used instead of **Am**.

Chord/Note fingering

Play all the chords in root position and above **middle c**, except the **A** and **A7** chords which can be played across **middle c**. The left hand notes can be fingered with the thumb ① then ring finger ④, whether there's a chord change or not. Near the end of the chorus the fingering changes slightly. Watch out for the 7th chords and the temporary key changes involving minor to major chords.

Sunrise, Sunset

Is this the little girl I carried, is this the little boy at play?
a d f e d c♯ e d a a a d f e d c♯ e d

I don't remember growing older, when did they?
d g b♭ a g f♯ a g d e e e

When did she get to be a beauty, when did he grow to be so tall?
 a d f e d c♯ e d a a d f e d c♯ e d

Wasn't it yesterday when they were small?
 d g b♭ a g f♯ a g g♯ a

Chorus

Sunrise, sunset, sunrise, sunset, swiftly flow the days
 f g f e f g f e f g f g a

Seedlings turn overnight to sunflowers
b♭   b♭   b♭ b♭ a g b♭ a f

Blossoming even as we gaze.
 g g g g f e f d

SUNRISE, SUNSET

Words by Sheldon Harwick, Music by Jerry Bock

Verse

d	D$_m$	D$_m$	a	A	A	d	D$_m$	D$_m$	a	D$_m$	D$_m$
<u>1</u>	2	3	<u>1</u>	2	3	<u>1</u>	2	3	<u>1</u>	2	3
Is	this	the	little	girl	I	carr	-		ied?		
When	did	she	get	to be	a	beaut	-		y?		

d	D$_m$	D$_m$	a	A$_7$	A$_7$	d	D$_m$	D$_m$	a	D$_7$	D$_7$
<u>1</u>	2	3	<u>1</u>	2	3	<u>1</u>	2	3	<u>1</u>	2	3
Is	this	the	little	boy	at	play?					
When	did	he	grow	to be	so	tall?					

g	G$_m$	G$_m$	d	D	D	g	G$_m$	G$_m$	d	G$_m$	G$_m$
<u>1</u>	2	3	<u>1</u>	2	3	<u>1</u>	2	3	<u>1</u>	2	3
I	don't	re	-	member	grow - ing	old			er,		
Was	- n't	it		yester - day	when	they			/(*to End of Verse*)		

SUNRISE, SUNSET

(Continued)

(Repeat bars 1-11 of Verse) — bar 4

e	E	E	b	E7	E7	a	A	A	e	A7	A7
1	2	3	1	2	3	1	2	3	1	2	3
when			did			they?					

End Of Verse

e	E	E	a	A	A	e	A	A	a	A7	A7	e	A7	A7
1	2	3	1	2	3	1	2	3	1	2	3	1	2	3
were			small.											

Chorus

d	Dm	Dm	a	A	A	d	Dm	Dm	a	A7	A7
1	2	3	1	2	3	1	2	3	1	2	3
	Sun -	rise,		sun -	set,		sun -	rise,		sun -	set,

d	Dm	Dm	a	Dm	Dm	d	Dm	Dm	a	D7	D7
1	2	3	1	2	3	1	2	3	1	2	3
	swift -	ly		flow	the	days.					

g	Gm	Gm	c	C	C	f	F	F	c	F	F
1	2	3	1	2	3	1	2	3	1	2	3
Seed -	lings	turn	ov - er -	night	to	sun		-	flowers,		

e	Em	Em	a	A7	A7	d	Dm	Dm	a	Dm	Dm
1	2	3	1	2	3	1	2	3	1	2	3
bloss -	om -	ing	ev - en	as	we	gaze.					

ADDITIONAL SONGS

See page 17 for titles of songs suited to the 3-beat bass-chord style.

PATTERN VARIATIONS

The accompaniment for "In Dublin's Fair City" involves variations on the basic 3-beat bass-chord pattern. As well as including bass runs, a bass note is added on the halfbeat at the end of alternate bars:

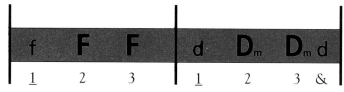

Occasional use of this 'leading' bass note can create a more varied sound.

THE BASS RUN

The run in the lead-in is a simple, on-the-beat bass run from the **c** note to the **f**. Bass runs can be used to 'join up' chords and at the same time make accompaniments more interesting.

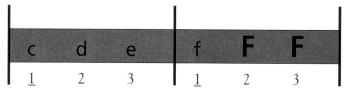

Your left hand ring finger ④ plays the **c** note, then the middle ③ plays the **d**, index ② the **e**, and finally the thumb ① plays the **f** note which begins the next bar. The same run of notes is used in bars 8 & 15 of the verse, but the timing is different:

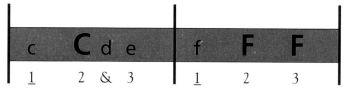

Here the **c** is played on the 1st beat of the bar as before, but a right hand **C** chord is then played on the 2nd beat. The **d** note is played between beats 2 & 3 and the **e** note on the 3rd beat.

Smooth & Steady Rhythm

To produce a smooth and steady rhythm needs concentration and a lot of practice. Commit the chords and keyboard notes to memory (if you haven't yet), and don't move your hands more than necessary - keep your fingers just above the keys and position your hands over the keys you're about to play. This is made much easier in Books 1 & 2 because only one hand is playing at any one time.

Chord/Note Fingering

The chords can be played in root position, and all above **middle c** apart from **C** & **Bb**. Your left hand can be held in the same position most of the time, with the thumb over the **f** note. For **bb**, move your little finger ⑤ down slightly, and for the **g** note move your thumb ① up slightly:

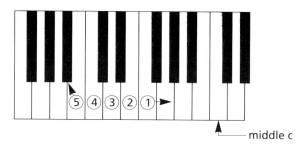

VAL DOONICAN

In Dublin's Fair City

In Dublin's fair city, where the girls are so pretty
c f f f f a a f g g g g bb

I first set my eyes on sweet Molly Malone
a a g f c bb a a g f g

She wheeled her wheelbarrow
c f f f a

Through streets broad and narrow
f g g g g bb

Crying "Cockles and mussels, alive alive oh"
a g a c b a c bb a f g f

(Chorus melody same as last 3 lines of verse)

Bass-Chord Style

IN DUBLIN'S FAIR CITY

Traditional, arranged by Russ Shipton

Lead-In

f	F	F	c	F	F c	f	F	F	c	d	e
1	2	3	1	2	3 &	1	2	3	1	2	3
											In

Verse

f	F	F	d	Dm	Dm d	g	Gm	Gm	c	C	C c
1	2	3	1	2	3 &	1	2	3	1	2	3 &
Dub -	lin's	fair	cit - y,		where the	girls	are	so	pre - tty,		I

f	F	F	d	Dm	Dm d	b♭	B♭	B♭	c	C	d e
1	2	3	1	2	3 &	1	2	3	1	2 &	3
first	set	my	eyes	on	sweet	Mol - ly		Ma -	lone.		She

f	F	F	d	Dm	Dm d	g	Gm	Gm	c	C	C c
1	2	3	1	2	3 &	1	2	3	1	2	3 &
wheeled	her	wheel -	barr - ow		through	streets	broad	and	narr - ow,		cry - ing
Chorus: live		a - live	oh,		a -	live		a - live	oh,		cry - ing

(Repeat last 8 bars for Chorus)

f	F	F	d	Dm	Dm d	c	C	d e	f	F	F
1	2	3	1	2	3 &	1	2 &	3	1	2	3
"Cockles		and	mussels		a -	live,	a - live -	oh".	*Chorus:* A -		

ADDITIONAL SONGS

When you've mastered the accompaniments for the last two songs, try the same ideas for the 3-beat songs given in Book 1, like "The Wild Rover", "My Bonnie" and "Bachelor Boy". The bass-chord style tends to suit songs of a mid-tempo or fast tempo, like those listed here. The last two songs are usually written in what's known as 12/8 rhythm - one bar can be split into four 3-beat patterns.

LIVERPOOL LOU (The Scaffold)
MISTLETOE AND WINE (Cliff Richard)
ON TOP OF OLD SMOKY (Traditional)
MAIDS WHEN YOU'RE YOUNG (Traditional)
DOWN IN THE VALLEY (Traditional)
MY FAVOURITE THINGS (from "The Sound of Music")
LUCILLE (Kenny Rogers)
HAPPY XMAS (WAR IS OVER) (John Lennon)
YOU'VE GOT TO HIDE YOUR LOVE AWAY (The Beatles)
BABY'S IN BLACK (The Beatles).

BASS RUNS IN G

There are three different bass runs in the accompaniment for "Congratulations":

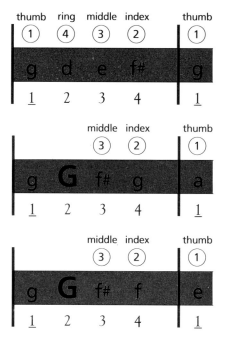

The fingering is given above each run. The first two runs should be played over an octave lower than **middle c**. The third run is 'chromatic'; i.e. it moves semitone by semitone and involves notes outside the **G** major scale as well. The left hand fingering for this run may seem strange - the run goes down in pitch while the fingers go left to right! This is necessary for the thumb to land on the **e** note for the start of the next bar - the fingers go slightly behind each other.

Chord/Note Fingering

All chords are in root position. Play **G, A & A7** across **middle c**, but for variety play **G** in the verse an octave higher. **D, D7, E & E7** are played just above **middle c**. Stop the chords a little for a springy, jumpier rhythm.

The left hand notes in the main pattern are fingered as in Book 1 - the thumb ① for the root note then ring finger ④ for the lower note on the 3rd beat.

CLIFF RICHARD

Congratulations

Congratulations, and celebrations
d e f#g d g gf# a e

When I tell everyone that you're in love with me
 e f#g b a a g   g f# e f# d

Congratulations, and jubilations
d e f#g d g gf# a e

I want the world to know I'm happy as can be
e f# g b a a g g f#e f# g

Who would believe that I could be happy and contented?
 g   f# e d   d d d   d e d b c e d

I used to think that happiness hadn't been invented
g f#e d   d   d d d d e d b c e d

But that was in the bad old days before I met you
 g f# f e e e   e g g a b d c

When I let you walk into my heart.
 f# g b a   e e e f# g a

CONGRATULATIONS
Words and Music by Bill Martin and Phil Coulter

Chorus

*

g	G	d	G	g	d	e	f#	g	G	d	G	g	G	f#	g
1	2	3	4	1	2	3	4	1	2	3	4	1	2	3	4

1.
2. me.

Con - grat - u - lat - ions,   and cel - e -
Con - grat - u - lat - ions,   and jub - i -

18

Bass-Chord Style

CONGRATULATIONS
(Continued)

(Repeat 8 bars)

a A e A	a A₇ e A₇	d D a D	d D₇ a D₇
1 2 3 4	1 2 3 4	1 2 3 4	1 2 3 4
brat - - ions,	when I tell	ev' - ry one that	you're in love with
lat - - ions,	I want the	world to know I'm	happ - y as can

(Stop)   *Verse*

g G d G	g	d D a D	d D₇ a D₇
1 2 3 4	1 2 3 4	1 2 3 4	1 2 3 4
be.	Who would be -	lieve that I could be	happ - y and con -

g G d G	g G d G	d D a D	d D₇ a D₇
1 2 3 4	1 2 3 4	1 2 3 4	1 2 3 4
ten - ted?	I used to	think that happi - ness	had - n't been in -

g G d G	g G f# f	e E b E	e E₇ b E₇
1 2 3 4	1 2 3 4	1 2 3 4	1 2 3 4
ven - ted.	But that was	in the bad old	days be - fore I

a Am e Am	a Am e Am	a A e A	a A₇ e A₇
1 2 3 4	1 2 3 4	1 2 3 4	1 2 3 4
met you,	when I	let you	walk in - to my

     ①   ④   *(to ✳)*

d D a D	d D a D	d D₇ a D₇	d d e f#
1 2 3 4	1 2 3 4	1 2 3 4	1 2 3 4
heart.			*Chorus.* Con - grat - u -

ADDITIONAL SONGS

See page 21 for more songs that suit the 4-beat bass-chord style.

Bass-Chord Style

BASS RUNS IN C

"Momma Don't Allow" is a traditional song using just the three main chords - in the key of **C** major this means **C**, **F** & **G**. The accompaniment includes bass runs by the left hand, 'joining up' the various chords to each other:

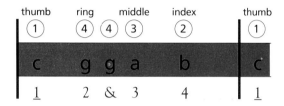

In a sense this run is played 'within' a **C** chord, but you could think of a **G** chord underlying the 2nd beat onwards. The extra **g** note on the halfbeat provides a little variety.

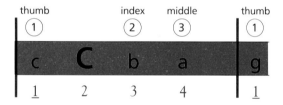

Here the thumb ① must pass underneath the index ② and middle ③ fingers. The run is down in pitch joining up the **C** chord to the following **G** chord.

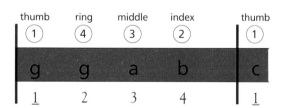

This time the underlying chord for the whole 1st bar is **G**. Here the thumb ① plays the first **g** note, but the ring finger ④ plays the next to begin the run.

Chord/Note Fingering

All chords can be played in root position, **C** using middle **c**, **G** across middle **c**, and **F** above **middle c**. The left hand notes (other than bass runs) involve the thumb ① and the ring finger ④ as usual.

CHORD ANALYSIS

When analysing chords, the different notes are named according to their scale position. It is useful for you to remember the chord note names. Here are major and minor chord examples:

*The **G** Major Chord (**G**)*

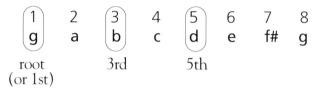

*The **G** Minor Chord (**Gm**)*

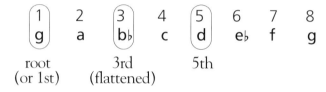

Thus the main note of a chord is the '1st' or 'root', the next note is called the '3rd' (because the interval from the root to that note is a 3rd), and the other note is the '5th' (because it's a 5th interval from the root). A '7th' chord involves four notes:

*The **G** Dominant 7th Chord (**G7**)*

1	2	3	4	5	6	7	8
g	a	b	c	d	e	f	g
root (or 1st)		3rd		5th		7th	

As you've seen already, the right hand 7th chord shape may omit the root note - the left hand will normally play a low root note in this case.

Momma Don't Allow

Momma don't allow no banjo playin' round here
  c c   c   c c c e e e d   c   c

Momma don't allow no banjo playin' round here
   g g   g g g g b b b a   g   g

Well I don't care what momma don't allow
  g g g   g   g   b b   b b a

Gonna play my banjo anyhow
  c c c   c   c c e e d c

Momma don't allow no banjo playin' round here.
  c c   c   c c c g g a a   b   c

Bass-Chord Style

MOMMA DON'T ALLOW
Traditional, arranged by Russ Shipton

Lead-In

c C g C | c g g a b

1 2 3 4 | 1 2 & 3 4

Verse

c C g C

1 2 3 4

Momma don't a - llow no

c C g C | c C g C | c g g a b

1 2 3 4 | 1 2 3 4 | 1 2 & 3 4

ban - jo playin' round here.

c C g C | c C b a | g G d G

1 2 3 4 | 1 2 3 4 | 1 2 3 4

Momma don't a - llow no ban - jo playin' round here.

g g a b | c C g C | c C d e

1 2 3 4 | 1 2 3 4 | 1 2 3 4

Well, I don't care what momma don't a - llow, gonna

f F c F | f F e d | c C g C

1 2 3 4 | 1 2 3 4 | 1 2 3 4

play my ban - jo an - y - how. Momma don't a - llow no

g g a b | c C g C | c g g a b

1 2 3 4 | 1 2 3 4 | 1 2 & 3 4

ban - jo playin' round here.

ADDITIONAL SONGS

Try adding bass runs to the 4-beat bass-chord songs given in Book 1, or those listed here.

HELLO MARYLOU (Rick Nelson)
I'VE JUST SEEN A FACE (The Beatles)
HELP (The Beatles)
DEDICATED FOLLOWER OF FASHION (The Kinks)

BILL BAILEY (Traditional)
YOU ARE MY SUNSHINE (Traditional)
HARD TRAVELLING (Woody Guthrie)
THAT'S ALL RIGHT (Elvis Presley)
THE BOXER (Paul Simon)
REASON TO BELIEVE (Tim Hardin)
PICK A BALE OF COTTON (Traditional).

A NEW 3-BEAT PATTERN

In Book 1 the arpeggio patterns began with a low left hand bass note and then a series of right hand chord notes. The pattern for the next accompaniment creates more interest by putting another bass note at the end of the bar:

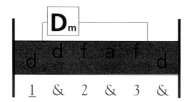

When the same chord is played for two bars, the 5th chord note (played *below* the root) can be used i.e. **a** for the **Dm** chord, as in bars 4 & 5.

BASS RUNS

Instead of using the root or 5th chord note, another scale note can be used to create a short bass run to the root note of the next chord (as in bar 1):

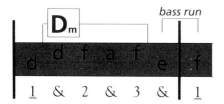

Two right hand notes are replaced by left hand run notes in bar 10:

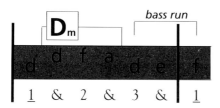

The same run is done in reverse two bars later.

Chord Positions

The chord indications placed above each bar will help you to follow the chord sequence. The C and Am chords include **middle c**, while the other chords are played above **middle c**. All chords are played in root position for this accompaniment.

Note Fingering

More interesting patterns with varied bass notes and runs, means the left hand fingering is more complicated. One way of handling the left hand notes is given above the notes of the accompaniment (①= thumb, ②= index etc.). Experiment with other ways of fingering to see if you'd prefer different left hand moves.

Note Length

The low root notes at the start of each bar can be allowed to ring on under the right hand chord notes that follow - experiment!

Scarborough Fair

Are you going to Scarborough Fair?
d d a a a e f e d

Parsley, sage, rosemary and thyme
a c d c a b g   a

Remember me to the one who lives there
d d d c a a a g f e d c

She once was a true love of mine.
d a g e e d c d

Notice the use of the out-of-key **G** major chord, and the melody note **b**. The 'expected' chord is **Gm** and 'expected' melody note **b♭** when in the key of **D** minor.

Arpeggio Style

SCARBOROUGH FAIR

Traditional, arranged by Russ Shipton

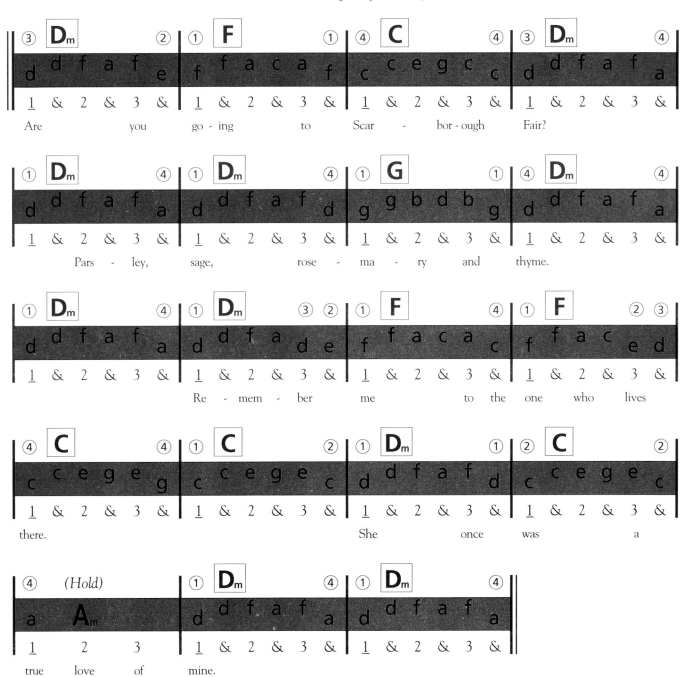

ADDITIONAL SONGS

Try adding bass notes and runs to the 3-beat songs given in Book 1. And here are a few more songs that are suited to the arpeggio style:

MEMORY (from "Cats")
THE SKYE BOAT SONG (Traditional)

ANNIE'S SONG (John Denver)
BIRD ON THE WIRE (Leonard Cohen)
IRENE GOODNIGHT (Leadbelly)
CATCH THE WIND (Donovan)
COME ALL YOU FAIR AND TENDER MAIDENS (Traditional).

23

TWO CHORD NOTES TOGETHER

Another variation of pattern and sound involves playing the first note of a right hand chord followed by the next two *together:*

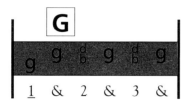

Hold your right hand over **G** chord notes as usual, but this time the thumb ① plays the **g** followed by the index ② and ring finger ④ playing the **b** & **d** notes together. (When chord inversions are used, different fingers will play the two chord notes together.)

SLOW BASS RUNS

A popular way of creating interest in an accompaniment is a falling bass line - the first note of each pattern following on from the one before to produce a 'slow' bass run. *This means the left hand is not always playing the root note of the underlying chord.*

There are three of these 'slow' runs in the accompaniment for "Three Times A Lady". The first is **g** to **f** to **e** to **d#** (notice that the **f** & **d#** notes are out-of-key). The chorus run goes from **g** to **f#** to **f** to **e**, while the tag run is **d** to **c** to **b** to **a** to **g**. The fingering for these runs is straightforward - the thumb ① starts the run, the index ② plays the next run note, and so on.

Chord Inversions/Positions

As you saw in Book 1, switching round the right hand chord notes can make chord changes smoother. The accompaniment for "Three Times A Lady" includes a number of chord inversions. You'll be able to tell what kind of inversion is being used for the chord by checking the order of the notes (the chord is indicated above each bar to help you follow the sequence more easily).

In the verse, **G** is played just above **middle c**, while **Em** & **B** are played across **middle c**. In the chorus, **G** is again played above **middle c**, except the penultimate bar where it is played in root position

below **middle c**. The **D** is also played above **middle c**, while the **F, C, Am** & **D7** chords all include the **middle c** note. The **B7** & **D7** chords indicated by a large chord letter can be played with the thumb over root & 7th notes.

To get the feel of the new pattern and the chord sequence, you could at first use root positions for all the basic major and minor chords.

THE COMMODORES

Three Times A Lady

Thanks for the times that you've given me
   b   b   b   b   c d   g g a

The mem'ries are all in my mind
  d   b b   a cbg ga   g

And now that we've come to the end of our rainbow
   d   b   b   b   b c d d c b a g

There's something I must say out loud
   d   b b   a c b ga g

You're once, twice, three times a lady, and I love you
   d   b a b   b   c b a g e c baged a

Yes you're once, twice, three times a lady
  b   c   b   a b   d   d   d d g

And I love you, I love you.
   e c bcd cba c baged ag

THREE TIMES A LADY

Words and Music by Lionel Richie

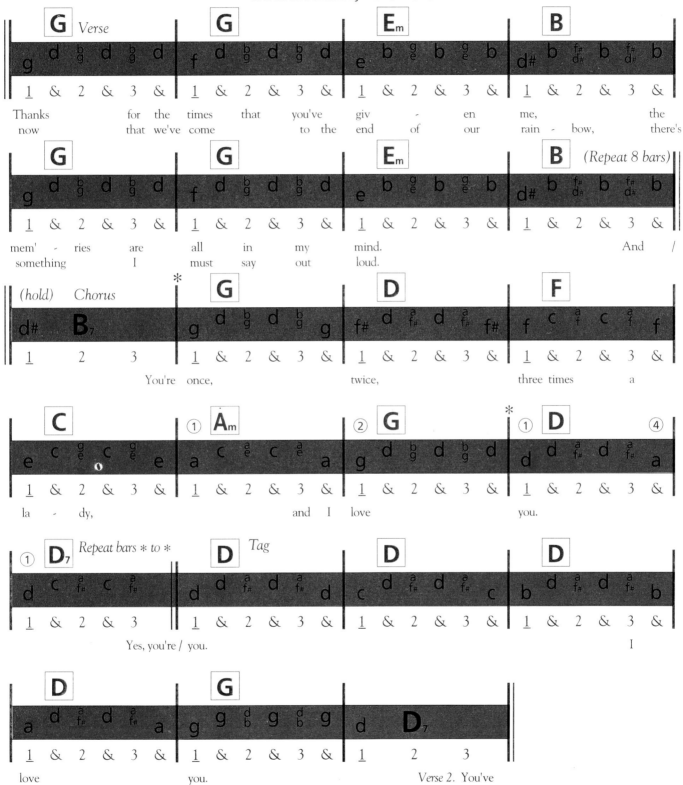

ADDITIONAL SONGS

See page 23 for additional 3-beat arpeggio style songs.

Arpeggio Style

A NEW 4-BEAT PATTERN

As for the last accompaniment, this 4-beat pattern includes two chord notes played together:

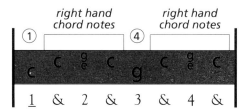

4-beat rhythm patterns often involves extra stress on the 3rd as well as 1st beat, and this is reflected by the low bass note on the 3rd beat.

A Pattern Variation

A slight variation to the above pattern is used in the second part of "Carrickfergus" - the last right hand note is replaced by a low left hand note, usually the 5th of the following chord, so it's a kind of 'leading' note. Move your left hand while the right hand is playing the notes on the 4th beat so the ring finger ④ plays the low 5th note - then the thumb ① is positioned over the root note to start the next bar.

Chord/Note Fingering

The chords can all be played in root position - but you can experiment with higher or lower octave positions for the **F**, **G** & **Am** chords.

The thumb ① and ring finger ④ are used for the left hand root and 5th notes - the 5th note is played lower than the root, as for "It Doesn't Matter Anymore" in Book 1. Move your thumb ① under your index finger ② for the run from **C** to **Am**.

Carrickfergus

I wish I was in Carrickfergus, only for nights in Ballygrant
c c b ad de f g e d c c d e f a bc d e c

I would swim over the deepest ocean, only for nights in Ballygrant
c c b a dde f g edc c d e f a bc d e c

But the sea is wide and I can't swim over
g g c b c c d e c dbg

Nor have I the wings to fly
g c d e dc f e d

If I could find me a handsome boatman
cc b a dde f g ed c

To ferry me over to my love and die.
c c d e f a b c d d c

CARRICKFERGUS

Traditional, arranged by Russ Shipton

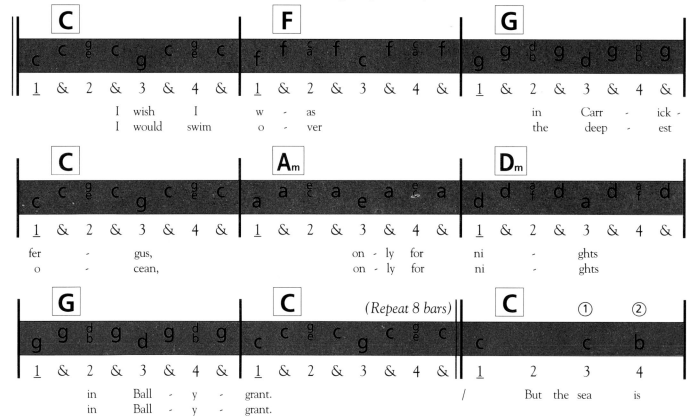

Arpeggio Style

CARRICKFERGUS
(Continued)

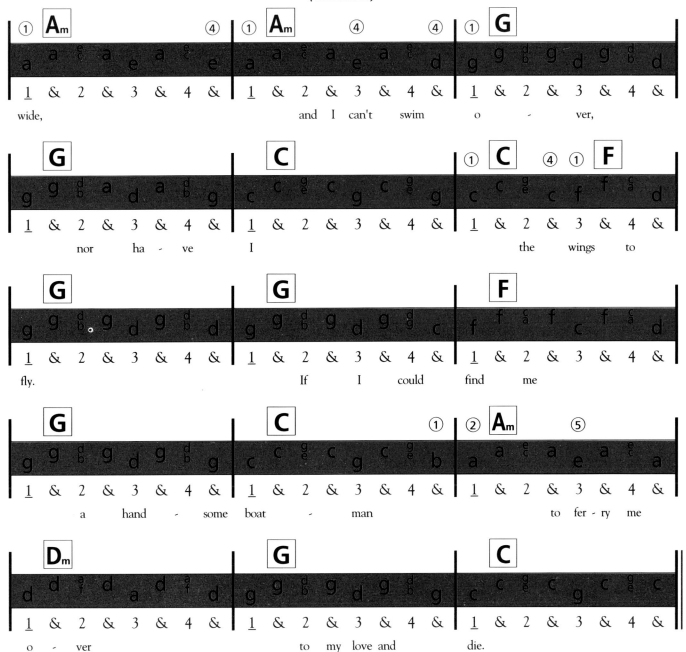

ADDITIONAL SONGS

The same kind of arpeggio you used above will suit the songs listed here - many have chord changes in the middle of the bar. The chord sequences for some of them are given in the back of the book along with the other words for "Carrickfergus".

RUBY TUESDAY (The Rolling Stones)
ALWAYS ON MY MIND (The Pet Shop Boys)
TURN! TURN! TURN! (The Byrds)
A WINTER'S TALE (David Essex)
BOTH SIDES NOW (Joni Mitchell)
HALFWAY TO PARADISE (Billy Fury)
THE LEAVING OF LIVERPOOL (Traditional)
SAILING (Rod Stewart)
IN AN ENGLISH COUNTRY GARDEN (Jimmie Rodgers).

MORE 7TH CHORDS

The 7th chords you've played so far are known in full as 'dominant 7th chords', like the D7, B7 & E7 in the next accompaniment. The position you used for these chords were 3rd inversions i.e. with the 7th note as the lowest note. Now try the root positions:

D7 (root position)

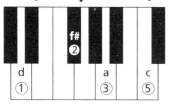

In a similar way, hold the B & E chords and add the 7th note (a & d respectively) to produce the dominant 7th chords.

Minor 7th Chords

Minor chords are also used in this accompaniment. These involve the same 7th note as the dominant 7th chords:

Am7 (root position)

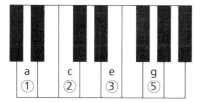

Now work out the Bm7 & Em7 chords by taking Bm & Em and adding the 7th notes (a & d respectively).

Major 7th Chords

A third type of 7th chord is the 'major 7th' chord:

Cmaj7 (root position)

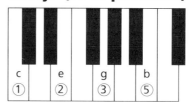

Convert G & F to Gmaj7 & Fmaj7 by adding f# & e respectively. Minor 7th and major 7th chords add a more diffuse, jazzy feeling to the accompaniment. (The 7th note for the dominant and minor 7th chord is 10 semitones above the root, but the 7th note for the major 7th chord is 11 semitones above the root.)

A New Pattern

So you can concentrate on the new chords, the pattern for the next song is kept simple - the left hand plays the low root note then 5th *above*, then the right plays across the chord and back again.

By The Time I Get To Phoenix

By the time I get to Phoenix, she'll be rising
f# g a a a g   a a   g d g b

She'll find my note I left hanging on her door
  g a a   a g a a   a g d b

She'll laugh when she reads the part, that says I'm leaving
  e   e   e   e e   e e c   d e d d

'Cause I've left that girl so many times before.
  a   b   c   c   c b a   g   g a

BY THE TIME I GET TO PHOENIX
Words and Music by Jim Webb

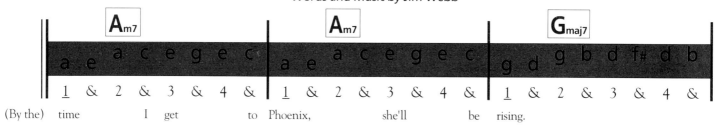

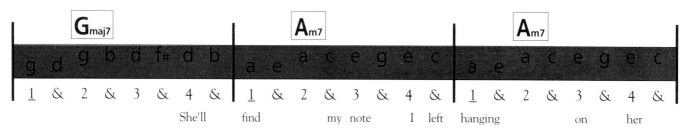

BY THE TIME I GET TO PHOENIX
(Continued)

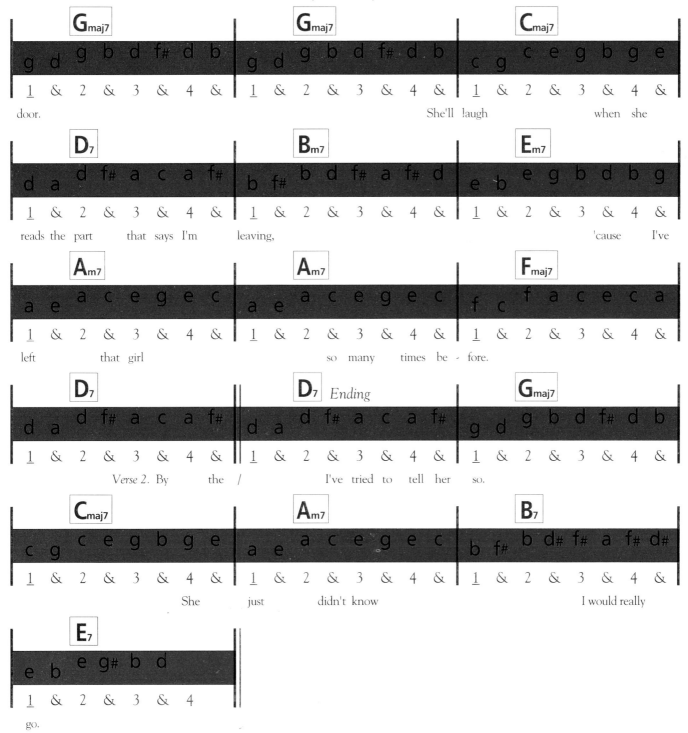

ADDITIONAL SONGS

Here are titles of songs that would suit the same kind of arpeggio pattern. Some involve 7th chords, but you can adapt the pattern for those that don't.

WHERE DO I BEGIN? (from "Love Story")

TRAINS & BOATS & PLANES (Burt Bacharach)
AFTER THE GOLDRUSH (Neil Young)
WONDERFUL TONIGHT (Eric Clapton)
SUZANNE (Leonard Cohen)
THE FIRST TIME EVER I SAW YOUR FACE (Roberta Flack).

Arpeggio Style

A SYNCOPATED PATTERN

So far you've stressed notes in the normal or 'expected' places i.e. on the beats. When stress is placed on the off-beat, this is known as 'syncopation'. Some mid-tempo ballads sound much better with a stress on the off-beat between the 2nd and 3rd beats of the bar:

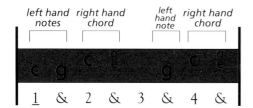

The left hand plays the root then 5th *above* with the ring finger ④ and thumb ①, then the right hand plays the **c** note of the **C** chord followed by the other two chord notes together. A stress on the off-beat is produced automatically because nothing is played on the 3rd beat (hold the two previous notes across this beat). Tap your foot and count the pattern carefully to produce the right rhythm.

Chord Positions

Play the chords in root positions to start with - except the **G7** where you can use the 3rd inversion. Once you've got the feel of the syncopated pattern and chord sequence, try using some inversions to cut down the hand movement.

ELTON JOHN

Sacrifice

It's a human sign when things go wrong
c c c e edc c   c e   d

When the scent of her lingers and temptation's strong
b b b b b b bc a a c e   d

Into the boundary of each married mind
bb b b b cc a   c e   d

Sweet deceit comes callin' and negativity lands
b b b b   b c a   a acce d

Cold cold heart, heart done by you
b   b bc   a   c e d

Some things look better, baby, just passin' through
b   b   b b c cg g   c e   d

And it's no sacrifice, just a simple word
d d d e e edc c cc e   d

It's two hearts living in two separate worlds
c c   c   c d b c   d cb   d c

But it's no sacrifice, no sacrifice, it's no sacrifice at all.
g c d e e edc e f f fed b c d ddcbc edc c

SACRIFICE

Words and Music by Elton John and Bernie Taupin

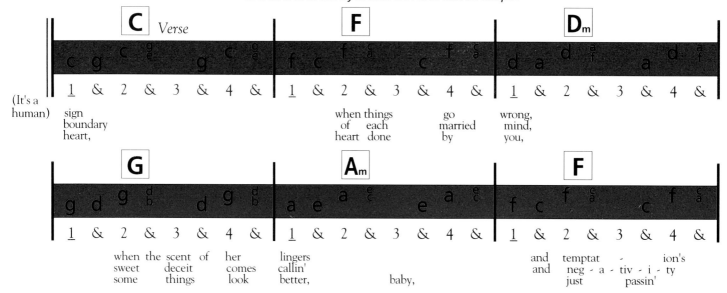

SACRIFICE
(Continued)

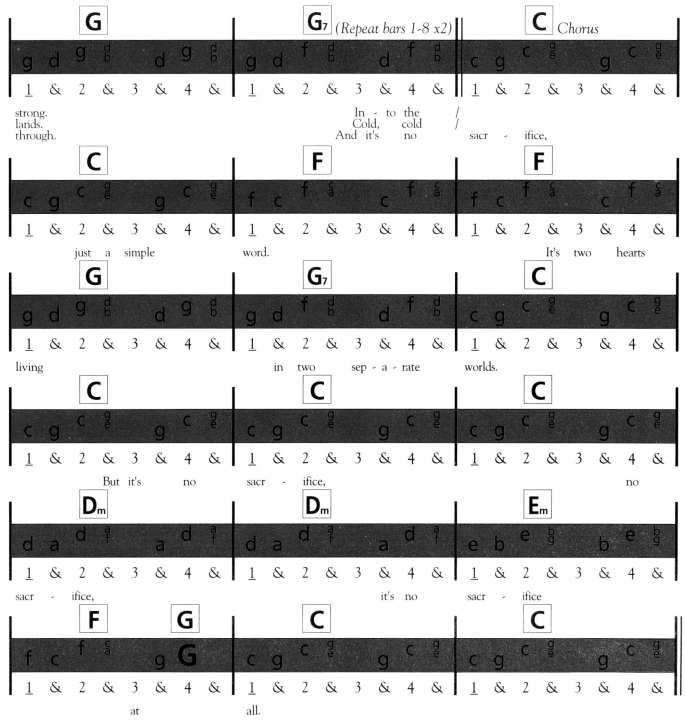

ADDITIONAL SONGS

A number of Elton John songs sound great with a syncopated pattern - some titles are given below, along with other well-known songs.

YOUR SONG (Elton John)
DANIEL (Elton John)

CANDLE IN THE WIND (Elton John)
THERE'S A KIND OF HUSH (Herman & The Hermits)
WILL YOU LOVE ME TOMORROW? (Carole King)
IF YOU COULD READ MY MIND (Gordon Lightfoot)
ALL MY TRIALS (Traditional)
SOMETIMES WHEN WE TOUCH (Dan Hill).

HOW TO PRODUCE A SWING

So far you've played accompaniments that all have a 'straight' rhythm i.e. where the off-beat notes are played *exactly halfway* between the beats. A swing is produced by delaying the notes between beats so they are played *just before* the following beat:

The delay of the left hand notes between beats is shown visually. It may help you to get the feel of the swing rhythm by saying 'u-pon' - the first syllable for the off-beat note and the second for the right hand chord.

Advancing The Root Note

The swing accompaniment pattern used for "Abilene" involves just two left hand low notes played between beats. One of these is an 'advanced' root note:

The root note of the following chord is advanced to the previous bar. In the example above, the left hand plays the **g** note at the end of the previous bar and the right hand plays the **G** chord on the 1st beat following. In the same way, the left hand plays the **b** note just before the **B** chord is played by the right hand on the first beat of the next bar.

Two Chords Per Bar

The kind of pattern used for "Abilene" is also fine for swing songs - blues or pop - that involve two chords per bar. The start of "Don't It Make My Brown Eyes Blue", for example, would look like this:

Chord/Note Fingering

The lead-in involves some quick chord changes. (This kind of 2-bar sequence is known in blues music as a 'turnaround', and is used as an introduction as well as a tag to lead back to the next verse). Use either the root position or the 3rd inversion for the **G7** chord - the same applies to the other dominant 7th chords in the accompaniment.

When changing from the **C** chord to **Cm**, just move your index ② one key to the left:

The Cm Chord (root position)

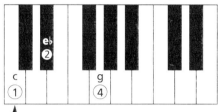

The basic major chords can all be played in root position. Only the **D** chord need be played above **middle c** here, but you could experiment with different octaves.

Abilene

This old but melodic blues piece provides a suitable introduction to the swing rhythm. The southern states of the U.S.A. saw the emergence of blues music at the turn of the century - and with it the birth of the 'swing' rhythm.

Abilene, Abilene, prettiest town I've ever seen
  b b b b b a   g g g g e gg d
People there don't treat you mean, in Abilene, my Abilene.
  a a   a   a f# a d   d e d g g g e g

General

Play the accompaniment at a relaxed, slow to medium pace, with an easy swing. You don't have to stop any of the notes or chords short - in fact the root notes can be held for one or even two beats under the following chords.

Swing Style

ABILENE

Traditional, arranged by Russ Shipton

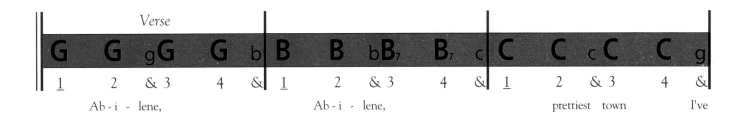

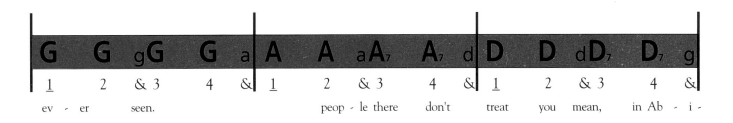

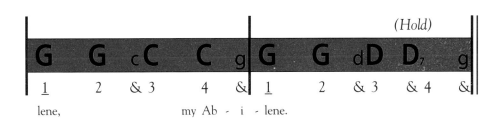

Note: Watch out for the quick chord change from **D** to **D7** on the half-beat in the last bar.

ADDITIONAL SONGS

The kind of swing pattern used for "Abilene" will suit the songs listed opposite. The chord sequences for some of them are given in the back of the book together with the other verses of "Abilene".

YOUR MOTHER SHOULD KNOW (The Beatles)
HONEY PIE (The Beatles)
SINGIN' IN THE RAIN (Gene Kelly)
SUMMERTIME (Al Martino)
HE'S GOT THE WHOLE WORLD (Traditional)
FRANKIE AND JOHNNY (Traditional)
EVERYTHING IS BEAUTIFUL (Ray Stevens).

THE KEY OF D MAJOR

Another key you'll often come across is **D** major.
This involves two black key notes:

D Major Scale: d e f# g a b c# d

Expected Chords: D Em F#m G A Bm

Try working out the root position for the only chord you haven't used yet: **F#m**.

Chord/Note Fingering

Notice that the low notes are the 5th notes of the chords - play them over an octave lower than the right hand chord position. The chords can all be played in root position to start with. To reduce right hand movement you could try playing the 2nd inversion of the **G** (**d g b**) and **A** (**e a c#**) chords. The **A7** can be played like this:

A7 (2nd Inversion)

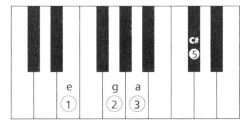

Rock Songs With A Swing

The swing rhythm began with blues music, but has spread to many other forms of music, including rock. The pattern for "Hi Ho Silver Lining" should be swung - delay the left hand notes till just before

the following chord, as you did for "Abilene":

D	D	aD	aD	a
1	2	& 3	& 4	&

For 'attack' and a dynamic rock rhythm, hit the notes hard and stop them short - chords *and* left hand notes should be stopped.

JEFF BECK

Hi Ho Silver Lining

You're everywhere and no-where, baby, that's where you're at
f# a a a   a a a   a f# b   b b b

Rolling down a bumpy hillside in your hippy hat
c c   c c c c b b a g a a a

Flying across the country and getting fat
a a a a   a a   a b b b b

Saying everything is groovy when your tyres are flat
c b c b c c   b b d c# d c# d e

And it's hi, ho, silver lining, and away you go, now baby
d e e f# f# f#e d e d c d d e c# d e

I see the sun ain't shining
f# f# f# f# e d e

But I won't make a fuss, though it's obvious.
d d b   d d a   g   a g f# f#

HI HO SILVER LINING

Words and Music by Scott English and Lawrence Weiss

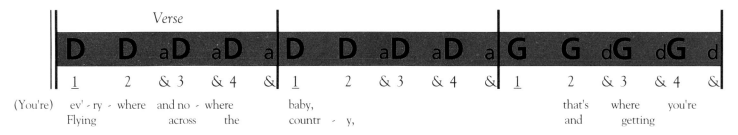

Verse														
D	D	aD	aD	a	D	D	aD	aD	a	G	G	dG	dG	d
1	2	& 3	& 4	&	1	2	& 3	& 4	&	1	2	& 3	& 4	&

(You're) ev'-ry-where and no-where   baby,   that's   where   you're
Flying   across   the   countr - y,   and   getting

Swing Style

HI HO SILVER LINING

(Continued)

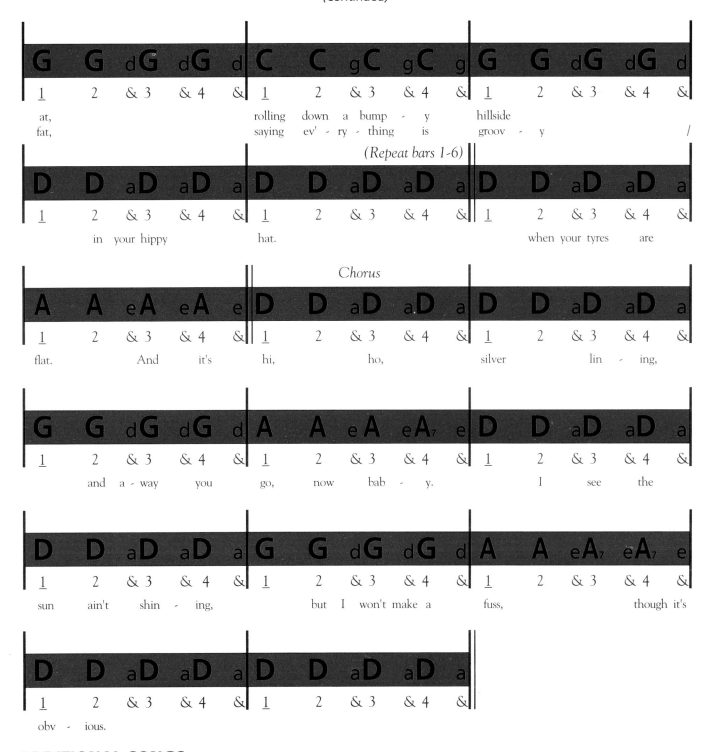

ADDITIONAL SONGS

The driving swing rhythm pattern with heavy stopped chords on all beats will suit these songs:

YELLOW SUBMARINE (The Beatles)
WITH A LITTLE HELP FROM MY FRIENDS (The Beatles)

DON'T STOP (Fleetwood Mac)
FLOWERS IN THE RAIN (The Move)
MELLOW YELLOW (Donovan)
SUNNY AFTERNOON (The Kinks)
GOD ONLY KNOWS (The Beach Boys).

Swing Style

COUNTRY SWING PATTERN

The swing rhythm is used for some blues, jazz, rock, pop, country and folk tunes (and reggae, which is looked at later in the course). Country and folk songs with a swing may suit this kind of pattern, a cross between bass-chord and arpeggio styles:

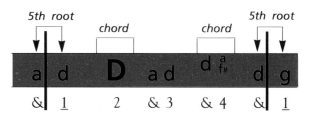

The 5th note *below* the root of the following chord is played by the left hand at the end of the previous bar (by the ring finger ④), then the left hand thumb ① plays the chord root note. The right hand chord is then played on beat 2, followed by the 5th and root left hand notes again. The right hand thumb ① and index ② & ring ④ fingers play the chord notes again, but separately this time. Finally the left hand moves up to position the ring finger ④ on the 5th of the following chord. The thumb ① then plays the root to start the next bar.

Remember to swing the off-beat notes by delaying them. You could also stop the chord notes on beats 2 & 4 to create more interest - but allow the other notes to ring on.

Chord/Note Fingering

The right hand chords can be played in root position above **middle c**, apart from **A7** & **G7** - use the 3rd inversion by moving your thumb ① one key to the left. The left hand bass run to start the verse can be played by the ring ④, then middle ③, then index ② fingers. The thumb ① completes the run by playing the root **d** note.

ROGER MILLER

King Of The Road

The middle section can be sung over the chord sequence for the first 8 bars of the verse:

Trailer for sale or rent, rooms to let, fifty cents
d a f# e f# g c# a b d d d

No phone, no pool, no pets, I ain't got no cigarettes
d a f# e f# g a a c# d e d c#

Ah but two hours of pushing broom
a b d a f# e f# g

Buys a eight by twelve, four-bit room
g e c# a b d d d

I'm a man of means by no means, king of the road!
f# a f# e d d d b e d c# d

Middle Section

I know every engineer on every train
d d d d d d d d c# b d b g

All of the children and all of their names
c# c# c# b a a b d b a

And every hand-out in every town
a a a f# e d b d b d b

And every lock that ain't locked when no-one's around, I sing ...
b a a a a c# c# c# e e e g f# e

KING OF THE ROAD

Words and Music by Roger Miller

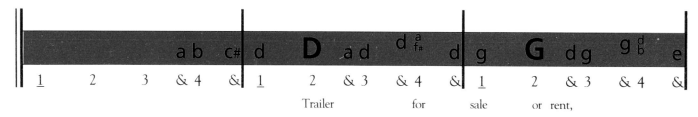

KING OF THE ROAD
(Continued)

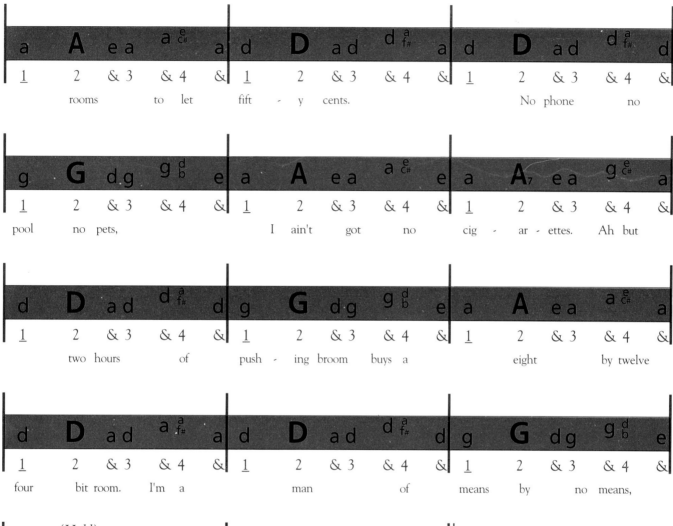

ADDITIONAL SONGS

Gentler, country swing songs will suit the kind of pattern used for "King Of The Road". Try playing some of the songs listed opposite with the same pattern.

LIVING DOLL (Cliff Richard)
RELEASE ME (Engelbert Humperdink)
WHO'S SORRY NOW (Connie Francis)
SUMMER HOLIDAY (Cliff Richard)
SONG SUNG BLUE (Neil Diamond)
DAYDREAM BELIEVER (The Monkies)
FROM A JACK TO A KING (Ned Miller)
MICHAEL ROW THE BOAT ASHORE (Traditional).

3-BEAT SWING PATTERNS

Some 3-beat swing songs will suit this pattern:

Either the root note of the previous chord or the next chord can be played at the end of the pattern - or no note at all. Titles of songs that would suit this kind of pattern are given separately on page 39.

The pattern used for "Mr. Bojangles" is an arpeggio kind involving two chord notes played together:

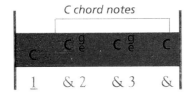

The left hand thumb ① plays the low root note, followed by the right hand thumb ① then fingers ② & ④ play the chord notes. Sometimes the last right hand note is replaced by a left hand note.

Bass Runs

The fingering for the slow bass run at the start of the verse is indicated. Hold your right hand in the C chord position while the left hand plays the descending bass line. Though the f# is used instead of the f in the slow run before the chorus, the fingering is the same. There is a 'fast' run in the 8th bar which you can use at the start as a lead-in. Follow the fingering shown. After repeating the 8 bars, play the usual G bar without the run.

Chord/Note Fingering

In the verse, use the root position for the C chord, then the 2nd inversions of the F & G chords. The D chord in the verse can be played in the root position, then move your thumb ① from the d to the c note for the D7 chord. The Am and G chords in the chorus can be played in root position, across middle c - in other words lower down.

The accompaniment for "Mr Bojangles" should be played smoothly, with no stopping of notes.

Mr. Bojangles

I knew a man, Bojangles, and he danced for you, in worn out shoes
g e d e   e e d e e   d c a a g   g

With silver hair, a ragged shirt & baggy pants, the old soft shoe
 g   e d e e e d   e e e d   c   a a g   g

He jumped so high, jumped so high, then he lightly touched down
 a   b   a g   e   d e d c   e   e e   d c   d

Mister Bojangles, Mister Bojangles, Mister Bojangles, dance.
 a a b g e d a a b g e d   a a b g e d   c

MR. BOJANGLES
Words and Music by Jerry Jeff Walker

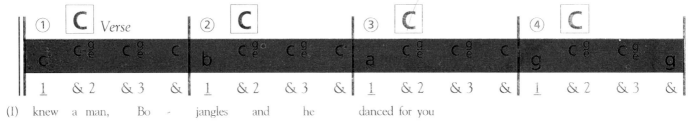

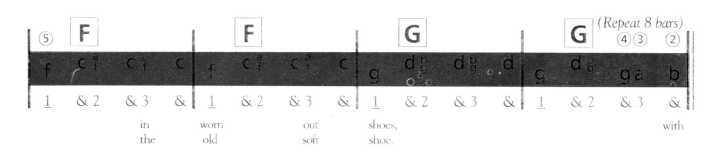

MR. BOJANGLES
(Continued)

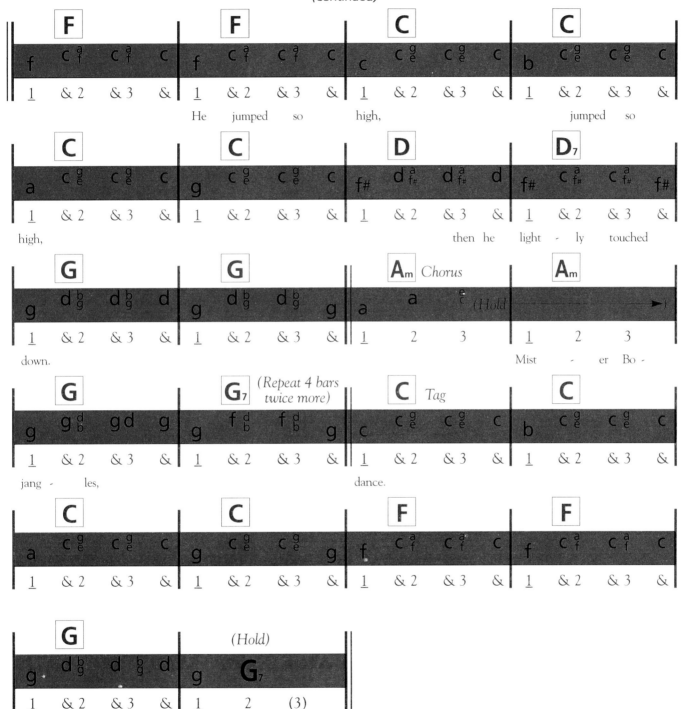

ADDITIONAL SONGS

(Arpeggio Swing)
THERE GOES MY EVERYTHING (Elvis Presley)
I NEVER WILL MARRY (Traditional)
IT'S FOUR IN THE MORNING (Faron Young)
MULL OF KINTYRE (Paul McCartney)
ARE YOU LONESOME TONIGHT (Elvis Presley)

(Chord Swing)
CLEMENTINE (Traditional)
WHAT THE WORLD NEEDS NOW IS LOVE (Burt Bacharach)
TAKE IT TO THE LIMIT (The Eagles)
THE LAST WALTZ (Engelbert Humperdink)
HAPPY BIRTHDAY TO YOU (Traditional).

A NEW PATTERN

In Book 1 you played a straightforward and symmetrical pattern for the song "The Locomotion". Switching the position and number of notes and chords can create a more interesting effect:

Count the pattern carefully, and stop the note between the 2nd & 3rd beats. Let the other notes and chords ring on. This is the pattern used throughout the accompaniment for the great soul/rock song "Stand By Me". Play it over and over until you remember it easily and can play it smoothly.

Pattern Variations

When you can play "Stand By Me", try varying the position and number of notes/chords. Here are two examples, both of which involve syncopation:

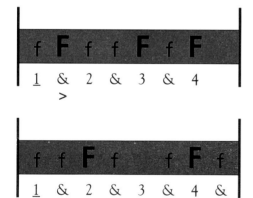

The sign > means you should stress the note/chord above it. Try these patterns for the songs listed on page 41.

Bass Runs/Chord Fingering

Similar bass runs to those used so far are included in this accompaniment. One way of fingering them is shown above the notation. The chords can be fingered in root position - F & Dm above **middle c** and B♭ across it.

BEN E. KING

Stand By Me

When the night has come and the land is dark
a c d a c f g a g f

And the moon is the only light we'll see
f g a f a gf g f f

No I won't be afraid, no I won't be afraid
a c d   a c d cb♭ag fg a   f g f

Just as long as you stand, stand by me.
f g a f f a gf a g f

So darling, darling, stand by me, oh stand by me
c d c e e dcd d d cd agfga g f

Oh stand, stand by me, stand by me.
a g gf a g f   a g f

STAND BY ME

Words and Music by Ben E King, Jerry Lieber and Mike Stroller

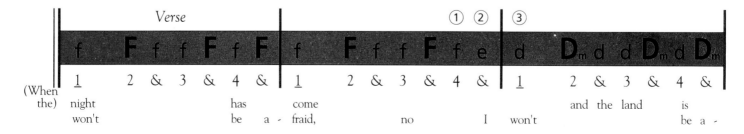

Rock Style

STAND BY ME
(Continued)

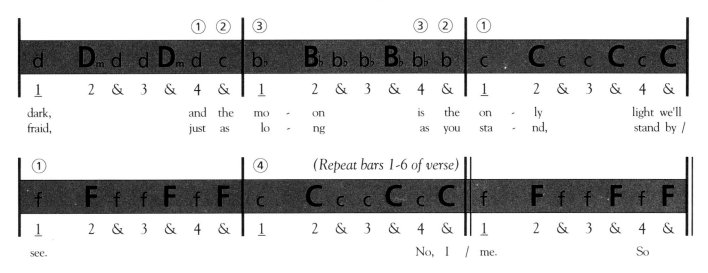

ADDITIONAL SONGS —

Here is a list of mid-tempo rock songs which suit the pattern you've just used for "Stand By Me". The chord sequences for some of them can be found at the back of the book, together with the second verse of "Stand By Me".

DOCK OF A BAY (Otis Reading)
IT'S TOO LATE (Carole King)
KNOCK ON WOOD (Eddie Floyd)
GIRLS JUST WANNA HAVE FUN (Cindy Lauper)
RESPECT (Aretha Franklin)
IN THE MIDNIGHT HOUR (Wilson Picket)
UNDER THE BOARDWALK (The Drifters).

41

Page 7

Page 9

GREENSLEEVES

Verse 2

```
   Am        C         G         Em
I have been ready at your command
      F       Dm          E         E7
To grant whatever your heart doth crave
Am      C         G        Em
I have wagered my life and land
      F         E    Am   Am
Your love and goodwill for to have.
```

Verse 3

```
   Am      C        G       Em
If you intend thus to disdain
      F         Dm       E     E7
It does the more enrapture me
     Am   C   G    Em
Yet even so I still remain
     F    E    Am Am
A lover in captivity.
```

Verse 4

```
        Am        C          G       Em
My men were all clothed out in green
        F       Dm       E      E7
And they did always wait on thee
Am     C     G      Em
I was also so gallant seen
       F         E          Am Am
And yet thou would not still love me.
```

Verse 5

```
        Am      C              G       Em
Now Lady Greensleeves, farewell, adieu
     F       Dm            E      E7
I pray the good Lord will prosper thee
      Am    C     G     Em
For I will always love you true
     F        E       Am     Am
Till you return and love but me.
```

MORNING HAS BROKEN

```
C   Am   Dm   G   F    C
C   Em   Am   D   G    G
C   F    F    C   Am   D
C   G    F    G   C    F    C
```

THE HOUSE OF THE RISING SUN

```
Am   C   D   F
Am   C   E   E7
Am   C   D   F
Am   E   Am  E7
```

THE FIRST NOEL

```
C    G    F    C
F    C    G7   C
C    G    F    C
F    C    G7   C
```
Chorus
```
C    G    F    C
Am   Em   F    C
```

THE QUEEN OF HEARTS

```
Am   F    Am   E7   Am
F    Dm   E7   Am   Am
F    Am   E7   Am   Am
F    Dm   E7   Am   Am
```

MOON RIVER

(There are no more lyrics for "Moon River")

TEARS

```
C   C    D   D
G   G7   C   C
A   A7   D   D
D   D    G   G7
C   C    D   D
G   G7   E   E
F   B7   C   A
D   G    C   G7
```

DIANE

```
C    G    G7   C
C    Dm   G7   C
C    G    G7   Am
Am   E    B    B7
E    G7   G7   G7
C    C    Dm   G7
C    C    G    G7
Am   D    C    G7
```

SAY WONDERFUL THINGS

```
C    C    G    G
G7   G7   C    C
C    C    F    F
C    G7   C    C
```
Chorus
```
C    C    F    F
G    G7   C    G7
C    C    F    F
C    G7   C    C
```

AMAZING GRACE

```
C    C    F    C
C    C    G    G7
C    C    F    C
C    G7   C    C
```

Page 11

HELP ME MAKE IT THROUGH THE NIGHT

Verse 3

```
D7                          G
   Yesterday is dead and gone
G                           C
   And tomorrow's out of sight
Am                 D
   And it's sad to be alone
D7                          G
   Help me make it through the night.
```

MY WAY

```
G    G      Dm   E
Am   Am     D    G
G    Dm     C    Cm
G    Am/D   Am   G
```
Middle Section
```
G    Dm     C    C
Am   D      Bm   Em
Am   D      Am   G
```

GREEN GREEN GRASS OF HOME

```
G    G    C    G
G    G    D    D7
G    G7   C    C
G    D    G    G
```
Chorus
```
G    G7   C    C
G    D7   G    G
```

THE WATER IS WIDE

```
G    G    C    G
G    G    C    D
D7   Bm   Bm   Em
C    D    D7   G
```

Additional Practice Songs

F	F	f	C	c	B♭		*Page 13*
1	2	&	3	&	4		

WILL YOU GO, LASSIE, GO?
Verse 2

      F   C   B♭ Dm
I will build my love a bower
          B♭   C   F
Near yon clear, crystal fountain
      B♭   C   Dm   Gm   Dm   B♭
And on it I will pile. All the flowers of the mountain.

Verse 3

        F   C B♭ Dm   B♭   C   F
If my true love, she were gone. I would surely find another
        B♭   C   Dm
To pull wild mountain thyme
     Gm   Dm   B♭
All around the bloomin' heather.

EVERYTHING I OWN
F	C	B♭	F/C
F	C	B♭	F/C
Gm	C	Gm	C
F/B♭	C	F/B♭	C
F/B♭	C	B♭	F

Middle Section
B♭	C	Dm	Dm
Dm	Gm	Gm	Gm
Gm	C		

KUM BA YAH
F	F/B♭	F	F
F	F/B♭	C	C7
F	F/B♭	F	F/B♭
F/C	F	F	

ETERNAL FLAME
G/Em	C/D	G/Em	C/D	
Em/B7	Em/A7	D/Bm	Am	Am/D

Middle Section
D/Dm	G/D	F/G	C/Am	
D/Bm	F/C	D	Em/B7	Em/A7

WHEN A CHILD IS BORN
F/C	F	F/Dm	C7	
B♭/C	Am/Dm	C/B♭/C	F	

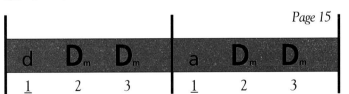

d	D_m	D_m		a	D_m	D_m	*Page 15*
1	2	3		1	2	3	

SUNRISE, SUNSET
Verse 2

 Dm   A   Dm Dm
Now is the little boy a bridegroom?
 Dm   A   Dm D7
Now is the little girl a bride?
 Gm   D   Gm Gm   E E7 A A7
Under the canopy I see them, side by side.
 Dm   A   Dm Dm
Place the gold ring around her finger
 Dm   A   Dm D7
Share the sweet wine and break the glass
 Gm   D   Gm E A A7 A7
Soon the full circle will have come to pass.

Chorus 2

Dm   A   Dm   A Dm Dm Dm   D7
Sunrise, sunset, sunrise, sunset, swiftly fly the years
   Gm   C   F F Em   A7   Dm Dm
One season following another, laden with happiness and tears.

d	D_m	D_m	d	*Page 17*
1	2	3	&	

IN DUBLIN'S FAIR CITY
Verse 2

        F   Dm   Gm   C
She was a fishmonger, but sure t'was no wonder
        F   Dm   B♭   C
For so were her father and mother before
              F   Dm
And they both wheeeled their barrow
           Gm   C
Through streets broad and narrow, crying etc.

Verse 3

        F   Dm   Gm   C
She died of a fever, no one could relieve her
        F   Dm   B♭   C
And that was the end of sweet Molly Malone
           F   Dm
But her ghost wheels her barrow
           Gm   C
Through streets broad and narrow, crying etc.

ON TOP OF OLD SMOKEY
F	B♭	B♭	B♭
B♭	F	F	F
F	C	C	C
C	F	F	F

MY FAVORITE THINGS
Am	Am	Am	Am
F	F	F	F
Dm	G	C	F
C	F	Dm	E7

Middle Section
Am	Am	E	E7
Am	Am	F	F
F	F	D	D7
C	F	F	G7
C	F	C	C

DOWN IN THE VALLEY
F	F	F	F
F	C	C	C7
C7	C	C	C7
C7	F	F	F
F	F	F	F
F	C	C	C7
C7	C	C	C7
C7	F	F	F

MAIDS WHEN YOU'RE YOUNG
F	F	F	C	C7	C7
F	F	F	C	C7	
F	B♭	F	C		
F	B♭	C	F	F	

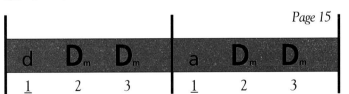

g	d	e	f#		g	*Page 19*
1	2	3	4		1	

CONGRATULATIONS
Verse 2

G   D   D7   G
I was afraid that maybe you thought you were above me
G   D   D7   G
That I was only foolin' myself to think you'd love me
G   E   E7   Am
But then tonight you said, you couldn't live without me
Am   A A7   D D D7 D7
That round about me you wanted to stay.

Additional Practice Songs

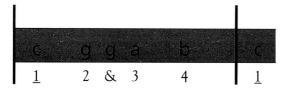

Page 21

c	g g a	b	c
1	2 & 3	4	1

Page 23

d	d f	a f	d
1 &	2 &	3 &	

MOMMA DON'T ALLOW

Verse 2

C   C   C C
Momma don't allow no guitar playin' round here
C   C   G G
Momma don't allow no guitar playin' round here
       C   C
Well I don't care what momma don't allow
               F   F
Gonna play my guitar anyhow
C   G   C
Momma don't allow no guitar playin' round here.

Verse 3

C   C   C C
Momma don't allow no boogie players round here etc.

Verse 4

C   C   C   C
Momma don't allow no rock 'n rollers round here etc.

SCARBOROUGH FAIR

Verse 2

Dm   F   C   Dm
Tell her to make me a cambric shirt
Dm   Dm   G   Dm Dm
Parsley, sage, rosemary and thyme
     Dm   F   F   C   C
Without a seam or fine needlework
     Dm   C   Am   Dm Dm
Then she'll be a true love of mine.

Verse 3

Dm   F   C   Dm
Tell her to wash it in yonder dry well etc.
          Dm   F   F   C C
Where never a drop of water fell etc.

Verse 4

Dm   F   C   Dm
Tell her to find me an acre of land etc.
       Dm   F   F   C C
Between the salt water and the sea strand etc.

Verse 5

Dm   F   C   Dm
Tell her to say when she's finished her task etc.
          Dm   F   F   C C
She should come to me, my hand for to ask etc.

REASON TO BELIEVE

C	F	C	C
F	G	C	C
D	D7	G	F
C	C	Am	F
G	G		

Middle Section

F	G	Am	C/G
G	F	G	Am
C/G	G		

HELLO MARYLOU

G	G	C	C
G	G	D	D
G	G	B	Em
A	D	G	G

Verse

G	G	C	C
G	G	D	D
G	G	C	C
G	D	G	G

SKYE BOAT SONG

G	G	Am	D
G	C	G	D
G	G	Am	D
G	C	G	G

Middle Section

Em	Em	Am	Am
Em	C	Em	Em
Em	Em	Am	Am
Em	C	Em	D

COME ALL YOU FAIR AND TENDER LADIES

G	C	G	D
Am	G	D7	G

DEDICATED FOLLOWER OF FASHION

C	C	F	F
C	C	F	F
B♭	B♭	F	D
Gm	C	F	F

Middle Section

C	C	F	F
B♭	B♭	F	F
B♭	B♭	F	D
Gm	C	F	F

PICK A BALE OF COTTON

F	B♭/F	F	C/F
F	B♭/F	F	C/F

Page 25

g	d ♭g	d ♭g	d
1 &	2 &	3 &	

BILL BAILEY

C	C	C	C	C	C	G	G
G	G	G	G	G	G	C	C
C	C	C	C	C	C	F	F
Dm	F	C	A	D	G	C	C

THREE TIMES A LADY

Verse 2

                G   G   Em   B
You've shared my dreams, my joys, my pains
             G   G   Em   B
You've made my life worth living for
             G   G   Em   B
And if I had to live my life over again, dear
        G   G   Em B B7
I'd spend each and every moment with you.

Additional Practice Songs

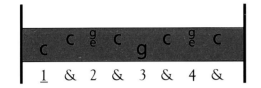

Page 27

CARRICKFERGUS

Verse 2

C   F   G   C
Now in Kilkenny, it is reported
Am   Dm   G   C
They've marble stones there as black as ink
C   F G   C
With gold and silver I would transport her
Am   Dm   G   C
But I'll sing no more now till I have a drink
C   Am Am   G
I'm drunk today, but then I'm seldom sober
G   C   C / F   G
A handsome rover from town to town
G   F   G   C
Oh but I'm sick now, my days are over
Am   Dm   G   C
Come all you young lads and lay me down.

ENGLISH COUNTRY GARDEN

D/G	A/D	D/G	A/D
D/G	A/D	D/G	A/D
D/A	D/A	D/G	A
D/G	A/D	D/G	A/D

THE LEAVING OF LIVERPOOL

C	F/C	C	G
C	F/C	C/G	C
Chorus			
G	F/C	Am/Em F/G	
C	F/C	C/G	C

A WINTER'S TALE

F	Bb	Am	Bb	
Bb	F/C	Dm	Bb	
C	F	Bb	Am	
Bb	Bb	F/C	Bb/C	F
Chorus				
F	F	C	F	
Bb	F	Bb	F	C
F	C	F	Bb	
F	C	F	F	

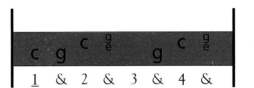

TRAINS AND BOATS AND PLANES

C	C	C	F
F	C	C	Am
Am	Am	Am	Am
Middle Section			
Am7	D7	Am7	D7
Am7	D7	Am7	D7
F	G	G	G

AFTER THE GOLDRUSH

G	C	G	C
G	D7	C	D7
G	F	C	F
G	D7	C	G
G	D7	C	G

WHERE DO I BEGIN?

Am	Am7	E	E7
Am	F	E	E7
Am	Am		
Am	Am7	E	E7
Am	F	E	E7
A	A7	Dm	G7
C	F	Bm/E7	Am
Dm	G7	C	F
B7	E	E7	

Page 31

SACRIFICE

Verse 2

                     C   F   Dm
Each misunderstanding after the fact
G   Am   F   G
Sensitivity builds their prison in the final act
G7   C   F   Dm
We lose direction, no stone unturned
G   Am   F   G
No tease too damning, when jealousy burns
G7   C
Cold cold heart etc.

THERE'S A KIND OF HUSH

C	E7	Am	C7
F	G	C	G7
C	E7	Am	C7
F	G7	C	C7
Middle Section			
F	F	F	F
C	C	C	C7
F	F	F	F
G	G	G	G7

WILL YOU LOVE ME TOMORROW?

F	Dm	Gm	C7
F	Dm	Gm	C7
A	A7	Dm	Dm
Gm	C7	Bb	F
Middle Section			
Bb	Bb	Am	Am
Bb	Bb	F	F7
Bb	Bb	Am	Am
Dm	G	Bb	C7

ALL MY TRIALS

C	C	C7	C7	C	C7	
F	F	C	Am	Dm	G7	C
Middle Section						
C	C	C	C	F	F	
C	Am	Dm	G7	C	C	

Page 29

BY THE TIME I GET TO PHOENIX

Verse 2

      Am7   Am7   Gmaj7 Gmaj7
By the time I make Albuquerque, she'll be working
      Am7   Am7   Gmaj7 Gmaj7
She'll probably stop at lunch and give me a call
Cmaj7   D7   Bm7   Em7
But she'll just hear that phone keep ringing
        Am7 Am7 Fmaj7   D7
Off the wall, that's all.

Verse 3

      Am7   Am7   Gmaj7 Gmaj7
By the time I make Olklahoma, she'll be sleeping
      Am7   Am7   Gmaj7 Gmaj7
She'll turn softly and call my name out low
    Cmaj7   D7   Bm7   Em7
She'll cry just to think I'd really leave her
       Am7   D7   Gmaj7 Cmaj7
Though time and time I've tried to tell her so
         Am7 B7   E D E Emaj7
She just didn't know I would really go.

Additional Practice Songs

Page 33

b	**G**		G	g**G**		G		b	**B**
&	1		2	& 3		4	&		1

ABILENE

Verse 2

G   B   /   B7
I sit alone most every night
C   G
Watch them freight trains roll out of sight
A   /   A7   D   /   D7
Wish that they were carrying me
         G/C   G/D7
To Abilene, my Abilene.

Verse 3

G   B / B7
Crowded city, there ain't nothin' free
           C   G
No there ain't nothin' in this town for me
A / A7   D / D7
I wish to God that I could be
         G/C   G/D7
In Abilene, my Abilene.

EVERYTHING IS BEAUTIFUL

F	Dm	G	G7
Gm	C7	F/Bb	F

Middle section

F	C	Bb	F	
F	C	Bb	F	
F	C	Bb	F	
F	C	Bb	F	F

FRANKIE AND JOHNNIE

C	C	C	C7
F	F	F	C
G	G7	C	C

SUMMERTIME

Am	Am/E	Am	Am
Dm	F	E	E7
Am	Am/E	Am	Am
C	D	Dm	Am
F	Am		

SINGIN' IN THE RAIN

G	G	G	G
G	G	D	D7
D	D	D	D
D	D7	G	G

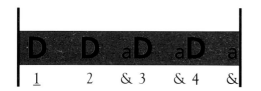

Page 35

D		**D**	a**D**		a**D**		a
1		2	& 3		& 4		&

HI HO SILVER LINING

Verse 2

  D   D G   G
Flies are in your pea soup, baby, they're waving at me
  C   G   D   D
Anything you want is yours now, only nothin' is free
  D   D G   G
Lies are going to get you someday, just wait and see
  C   G   D   A
So put up your beach umbrella, while you're watchin' T.V.

DON'T STOP

D/C	G	D/C	G
D/C	G	A	A7

(same for chorus)

FLOWERS IN THE RAIN

G	G	G	C/D
G	G	G	C/D

Chorus

G	G	G	D/D7
G	G	G	D/D7

Middle Section

G	C	G	Am
F/G	C	D/D7	

SUNNY AFTERNOON

Dm	C	F	C
A	A7	Dm	C
F	C	A	A7
Dm	Dm		

Chorus

D	D7	G	G7
C	C7	F	A
Dm	G	Dm	G/C
F	A	Dm	Dm
Dm	Dm	Dm	Dm

a	d	**D**	a	d	d d f#		d	g
&	1		2	& 3		& 4	&	1

Page 37

KING OF THE ROAD

Verse 2

D   G
   Third box car, midnight train
A   D
   Destination, Bangor, Maine
D   G
   Old, worn-out suit and shoes
A   A7
   I don't pay no union dues
              D   G
   I smoke old stogies I have found
A   D
   Short, but not too big around
        D   G
   I'm a man of means by no means
A7   D
   King of the road.

Middle Section

        D   G
   I know every engineer on every train
A   D
   All of the children and all of their names
        D   G
   And every handout in every town
        A
   And every lock that ain't locked and
  A7
No-one's around, I sing . . .

DAYDREAM BELIEVER

C	G	C	F
C	Am	D7	G7
C	G	C	F
C	F/G7	C	C

Chorus

F/G	Em	F/G	Am/F
C	F	C	D7	G7

MICHAEL ROW THE BOAT

D	D	G	D
D/G	A	D/A	D

LIVING DOLL

C	C	C	C
C	C	D/D7	G/G7
C	C	A/A7	D7/G7
C	F	C	C
F	C	C	C7
F	F	Dm	G/G7

SONG SUNG BLUE

G	G	D	D
D7	D7	G	G
G7	G7	G7	C	C
D7	D7	G	G
D	D7		

Additional Practice Songs

Page 39

C	C	cC	c	C	c g/e	c g/e	C
1	2	& 3	&	1	& 2	& 3	&

MR. BOJANGLES

Verse 2

     C   C   C   C
I met him in a cell in New Orleans I was
F   F   G   G
Down and out
       C   C   C   C
He looked to me to be the eyes of age
F   F   G   G
As he spoke right out
F   F   C C   C   C
He talked of life, talked of life
D   D7   G G
He laughed, slapped his leg a step.

Verse 3

       C   C   C   C
He said his name Bojangles and he danced a lick
F   F   G   G
Across the cell
       C   C
He grabbed his pants for a better stance
       C   C F   F   G   G
Oh he jumped so high, he clicked his heels
F   F   C   C   C C
He let go a laugh, let go a laugh
D   D7   G   G
Shook back his clothes all around.

Verse 4

       C   C   C   C
He said "I dance now at every chance at Honky Tonks
F   F   G   G
For drinks and tips
       C   C   C   C
But most the time I spend behind these county bars
F   F   G   G
'cause I drinks a bit"
F   F   C   C   C   C
He shook his head, and as he shook his head
D   D7   G   G7
I heard someone ask, "Please". . .

ARE YOU LONESOME TONIGHT

C	C	C	C
C	A7	Dm	Dm
Dm	Dm	G	G
G7	G7	C	C
C7	C7	F	F
D	D7	G	G7
C	C	D	D7
G	G7	C	G7

IT'S FOUR IN THE MORNING

C	C	C	C
C	C	G	G7
G	G	G	G
G7	G7	C	C
C	C	C	C
C	C7	F	F
F	G	C	Am
F	G7	C	C

CLEMENTINE

F	F	F	C
C7	F	C7	F

(same for chorus)

TAKE IT TO THE LIMIT

G	G	C	C
G	G	C	C
G	B	Em	Em
D	D	D7	D7
G	G	C	C
G	G	C	C
Am	Am	C	C
D	C	D	D7

Chorus

C	G	C	G
C	D	G	G

I NEVER WILL MARRY

C	G	C	C
F	G	C	C7
F	G	E	Am
D7	G	G7	C

Chorus

G	G	G7	G7
C	C	C	C7
F	F	G	G7
C	C	G	G7

Page 41

f	F	f	f	F	f	g
1	2	&	3	&	4	&

STAND BY ME

Verse 2

              F   F
If the sea that we look upon
Dm   Dm
Should tumble and fall
            Bb   C   F C
Or the mountain should crumble to the sea
         F   F
I won't cry, I won't cry
         Dm   Dm
No I won't shed a tear
         Bb   C   F
Just as long as you stand, stand by me.

IN THE MIDNIGHT HOUR

G/C	G/C	G/C	G/C	
G/C	G/C	G/C	G/C	
D	C	D	C	
G/C	G/C	G/C	F	D

THE DOCK OF A BAY

G	B	C	A
G	B	C	A
G	Em	G	Em
G	A	G	E

Middle Section

G/D	C	G/D	C
G/D	C/G	F	D

UNDER THE BOARDWALK

F	F	C	C7
Gm/C	Gm/C	F	F7
Bb	Bb	F	F
F	C/Bb	F	F

Chorus

Dm	Dm	C	C
Dm	Dm	C	C
Dm	Dm		

Conclusion

A NOTE FROM THE AUTHOR

Congratulations on getting halfway through the course! You now know enough keys, chords and rhythm patterns to arrange and play most of the songs you like. Even though the patterns you've mastered involve just one hand playing notes at any one time, you have acquired a wide spread of interesting and enjoyable styles. Try to learn two or more songs thoroughly in each style so your feel for the different patterns and chord changes becomes natural and flowing.

In Book 3 you'll be learning patterns which involve both left and right hands playing some of the notes at the same time. My simplified notation still remains simple and easy to read, but it is split into two lines - the top for the right hand chords and notes and the lower one for the left hand chords and notes. During the third book of the course you'll find that your playing becomes fuller sounding and has a more professional feel.

Enjoy your playing *and* learning,

Russ Shipton